The
AYURVEDIC
Diet

Reenita Malhotra Hora is a financial journalist and Ayurveda clinician based in Hong Kong. She anchors and produces *Money for Nothing*, Hong Kong public radio's live daily radio show about finance and investing. As a print journalist, she has contributed to Reuters, *South China Morning Post: Family Section*, *The Wall Street Journal*, *The New York Times*, CNN, *AsianInvestor*, *The Times of India* and *The Economic Times*.

She is the author of five books: *Inner Beauty, Ayurveda: The Ancient Medicine of India, Forever Young, Operation Mom* and *When Arya Fell through the Fault*.

The AYURVEDIC *Diet*

REENITA MALHOTRA HORA

HARPER
element

First published in India in 2016 by Harper Element
An imprint of HarperCollins *Publishers* India

Copyright © Reenita Malhotra Hora 2016

P-ISBN: 978-93-5177-532-4
E-ISBN: 978-93-5177-533-1

2 4 6 8 10 9 7 5 3 1

Reenita Malhotra Hora asserts the moral right
to be identified as the author of this work.

HarperCollins *Publishers*
A-75, Sector 57, Noida, Uttar Pradesh 201301, India
1 London Bridge Street, London, SE1 9GF, United Kingdom
Hazelton Lanes, 55 Avenue Road, Suite 2900, Toronto, Ontario M5R 3L2
and 1995 Markham Road, Scarborough, Ontario M1B 5M8, Canada
25 Ryde Road, Pymble, Sydney, NSW 2073, Australia
195 Broadway, New York, NY 10007, USA

Typeset in 12/14.9 Arno Pro
Jojy Philip New Delhi 110 015

Printed and bound at
Thomson Press (India) Ltd

For my late grandmother Pushpa Vij
who taught me that flavour is the mother of medicine

Contents

Introduction

A Personal Story

About a hundred years ago, there was no such thing as 'Ayurvedic cuisine'. It's not like the people of India differentiated between the food coming out of their kitchens from the food that they separately referred to as 'healing cuisine'. On the contrary, pretty much all the food that came out of South Asia was a 'healing cuisine' prepared with seasonal ingredients to harmonize one's health with the changing elements of the season. In other words, back in the day, we had it right. Go figure!

Over time however, we found ourselves seduced by lifestyles outside South Asia – education, careers and certainly the cuisine. As Westernized eating patterns and the culture of fast food changed the makeup of our dining tables, we made the conscious decision to refer to the healing food as 'Ayurvedic cuisine'. In other words, it is a different way of eating from the modern fare in our kitchens, one that is based on the principles of Ayurveda, India's ancient system of holistic health.

I grew up in Bombay, the most dynamic perhaps of all Indian cities, still laced with the oldest of Indian traditions. Like so many around me, I grew up living Ayurveda without being actively conscious of it. In fact, it was the furthest thing from my mind when I set out for the US as a young student. As far as I was concerned, it was just routine in my household to prepare meals with the foods and herbs of the season. It didn't occur to me that our home cooking consciously harmonized our mind-body with the effects of the seasons. Or that in doing so, we were using food as medicine to prevent ill health and bring ourselves back to balance if ever we were 'pushed out of whack' with the environmental elements of the season. Who even knew what that meant?

It wasn't until I arrived at college in the States that I noticed the difference in the way we ate at home and what was served up in Western kitchens. In an atmosphere of intense competition and high expectations, I watched many of my friends survive on a never-ending cycle of fast food, frozen meals, processed foods, caffeine and Tylenol. Rather than listening to the demands of their own bodies, as I had become accustomed to, they were trying to override their need for adequate sleep, good nutrition and the feeling of natural energy by using synthetic solutions ... and it wasn't working. They told me over and over again that they felt tired, stressed out, depleted.

It was only then that I began to realize that all my life I had lived on something that other people referred to as 'medicine' – Indian medicine or Ayurveda – and how important it is for optimizing your health so you can feel your best all the time and not just on days when you have something special going on. Of course, I had lived all my life taking this ancient medicine for granted. So, after fighting my family to let me go to the States for my education, I surprised them again by returning home to India. It was only after I had completed my bachelor's degree that I decided I would study Ayurvedic medicine. I knew I would become a health educator and consultant and, above all, an ambassador for Ayurveda.

How I got to this point, this crossroad of so-called modern life and the ancient tradition of Ayurveda is perhaps not so different a story from anyone else's. Modern living aside, many of us have grown up under the loving umbrella of an extended family. It's a pretty basic Indian concept – no prizes then for guessing why Ayurvedic cuisine is often associated with dadi or nani's cooking.

My grandfather, Gopal Krishan Vij, was probably my first role model in self-sufficiency. He insisted that you could learn anything in the world, but if you did not know how to cook a basic meal to feed yourself then you were pretty much done for. So he put me under the trusting care of his wife. My grandmother, Pushpa Vij, was probably my first, and continues to be, my greatest influence when it comes to food and cooking. Her belief that the 'simpler' the preparation of food, the more the flavour, holds true, and it is this very flavour of the food that ultimately benefits your health. As a child I just didn't get what she meant by that – just how flavour had anything to do with medicine was too esoteric a concept for my rudimentary understanding. Later, as a student of Ayurvedic medicine, I learnt that different tastes have different energetic effects on the mind-body, and this is what ultimately impacts your health. It suddenly made perfect sense – after all, if you eat something that tastes good then you naturally feel good. And if you don't like the flavour of what you eat then naturally you are going to wince, scowl and complain about the after-taste. Pretty basic, huh?

My grandparents' wisdom made an indelible imprint on my life and nutritional values. Together they sustained a healthy-eating partnership – the backyard of their home had my grandfather's organic kitchen garden, tended solely by him; the kitchen was my grandmother's pride and joy, where she took the ingredients grown by my grandfather and transformed them into healing recipes.

They both bought into the notion that health, longevity and keeping your family in shape is the real purpose behind growing your own foods and preparing them in a healthy manner. Hence their unique blend of kitchen-garden values. They were the living legends of their own convictions, so much so that their food legacy thrives in my household even today – my grandfather's kitchen garden lives on in my own backyard and my grandmother's recipes continue to feed my husband and children. I subsequently pass this on to my clients and students of Ayurvedic cooking.

Of course, people in today's world are interested in eating right to stay in shape. That simple notion of staying in shape begs the question as to how it got so complicated in the first place. Most of us spend countless hours wondering how to be skinny, but that's a matter of pure vanity. Rarely do we give a thought to how poor food choices, bad eating patterns and being overweight can lead to so many commonplace illnesses.

It takes me back to when my husband and I first bought our home in California. It was a huge milestone in our life and so we did everything possible to guard and protect our prized property, but the one thing we just couldn't obtain was earthquake insurance and I kept thinking. How can that be? Wasn't this one of the world's most earthquake-prone territories? But the fact of the matter was that no provider wanted to give insurance because chances were that sooner or later, your home would be hit by an earthquake. At first we were alarmed by the predicament – after all the effort we had put into it, there was no way we could let our house fall down. Therefore, we grit our teeth and decided to self-insure our home by knocking it down and re-building everything from a rock-solid foundation.

It's that particular example which always reminds me of Ayurveda. As you grow older, your medical insurance premiums inevitably go up because as far as the providers are concerned, chances are that some kind of illness could hit you in your middle to upper years – just like that earthquake. And when it does, you know the costs will be horrendous. But such a calamity was inconceivable in the country where our ancestors had lived for centuries because they believed in a different kind of insurance – Ayurveda.

'Ayurveda as an insurance policy! How could that possibly work?' you might ask.

Here's the deal – our so-called modern living habits have caused us to programme our bodies to gorge on junk food and eat more on a daily basis than our bodies are designed to digest sugar like there is no tomorrow and we load ourselves with packaged foods that can be zapped into a meal in a matter of three microwave moments. Did you know that as compared to fifty years ago, sugar consumption in India has gone up from 5 to 13 per cent of sugar produced globally?* And all this loaded with more preservatives than natural ingredients. And you wonder why people are overweight or how they got saddled with all sorts of illnesses in the first place.

Have you ever paid attention to how your current diet and lifestyle affects your body, moods and energy levels? Right now, think about how you feel on most days. Sluggish perhaps? Bloated? Do you wake up tired with a desperate need for chai or coffee to get you going in the morning? Do you get cranky or crabby later in the day? Are you sleepy in the afternoons? Do you rely on colas or sweets to boost your mood? Do you wake up during the night and toss and turn into the wee hours of the morning? How does this make you feel the next day? Tired? Irritable? Ready to snap at your neighbour?

Now what if someone told you that you could reprogramme your body to eat healthy, that all you had to do was follow a relatively simple formula that might cause

---

* Reference article: http://timesofindia.indiatimes.com/life-style/ health-fitness/diet/Lakhs-of-Indians-becoming-sugar-dependent/ articleshow/19456525.cms

you to struggle initially, only because you're not used to it but a formula that, in a matter of days, would become a habit? What if you could actually change your eating habits to achieve that perfect body, health and optimum energy levels for the rest of your life? Would you do it? Sure you would because, guess what ... you are conditioned to be that way. Because it's the way our ancestors have been living for centuries.

That's the reason I chose to write this book, to help you get back to eating according to those basic old world dietary patterns that are going to help you self-insure your health. Let the name of this book not mislead you. Truth be told, Ayurveda is a lifestyle, not a diet. By embarking upon the eating guidelines set out in this book, you will basically be addressing a lifestyle change. While in the initial few weeks or a month, it could feel like a regimented diet, you should know that during this time what you are doing is pushing the reset button. You are effectively reprogramming your brain, your digestive tract and your taste-buds to eat the way you were naturally designed to from birth. Once you have got the hang of it, you'll love the way you feel with high energy levels and heightened sensory reactions. Your sleep will improve, you will have a higher sex drive and a better attitude at both work and play. You'll never want to go back to your terrible old eating habits because the new you will be the true you.

You might ask what it really means to eat according to the seasons; and since when does one divide up the calendar into six seasons rather than four?

Foodies and fitness fanatics alike tend to divide the year

into four seasons. Winter – the time for guiltless gorging on holiday treats; spring – the time to melt away your winter fat and prepare for summer; summer – the time to don your sleeveless top and shorts. And then there is fall – the time to justify gorging as you graduate from shorts and strapless t-shirts back to jeans and long-sleeved dresses!

It works perfectly for fitness media but truth be told, four seasons are a Western notion.

The Indian calendar divvies up the year into six basic seasons. According to Ayurveda, optimizing your health means eating foods that balance the elements of each season. Food preparation techniques, appropriate food selection and combination, proper eating habits all contribute to preventing ill health. And guess what? Despite the fact that Ayurveda is the oldest life science on the planet and you are pretty sure that, at some level, you have its philosophies hardwired into your DNA, I'll bet you didn't realize that following the fairly simplistic rules of the Ayurvedic diet can get you in shape for life.

For example, did you know that as long as you eat according to the season, you can maintain your ideal weight? Of course, that's not the case with most of us – we usually plan to eat as much as we want without really stopping to think about the season or our mind-body type. And did you know that doing a seasonal cleanse a couple of times a year in accordance with the changing seasons can help you keep the proliferation of your fat cells in check? Not to mention refuelling your immune system? Chances are you weren't aware, but again, it's basic Ayurveda.

This book shows you how to self-insure your health to be 'illness and overweight' proof just like we self-insured our home to be earthquake-proof. I will share with you the philosophy and practices of Ayurvedic cooking and demonstrate how easy it is to incorporate them into your kitchen so that you too can cultivate the same longevity.

The following pages are designed to enable you to achieve sustainability in your food and nutritional patterns through balanced, healthy Ayurvedic cooking. If you are determined to end the cycle of stress and exhaustion, and the toll they take on your health and appearance, then rest assured you are in good hands. All you need to do is make simple, sensible culinary changes. *The Ayurvedic Diet* is an introduction to the principles of Ayurvedic cooking, and details how to put them to work as you move towards eating healthy, fulfilling meals.

I should mention here that Ayurvedic medicine is both preventative as well as curative in its application. So terminologies like 'Ayurvedic diet' and 'healing cuisine' can be interpreted in a variety of ways. For example, when a person is ill, your Ayurvedic doctor is likely to put you on a restricted diet that will help cure you. This is vastly different from generally eating according to Ayurvedic principles to keep your health in check. There are several books out there that refer to specific Ayurvedic cures, but that's not what I cover here. I believe that the evolution of disease is unique to each person, so trying to cure yourself using a book is less than ideal. Deferring to an Ayurvedic health practitioner who can custom design a specific healing diet to your needs is probably the best path you can adopt if you are really unwell. This book is about Ayurveda as a preventative medicine. The assumptions here come from a place where readers are generally healthy and want to stay that way, or where readers are stressed and out of whack, and need a little help to get their fitness level back on track. It does not cater to the chronically ill who would be better served by checking into an Ayurvedic clinic or hospital.

Part I – The Ayurvedic Way of Life is designed to introduce Ayurveda to those who are less familiar with the subject. In the first chapter, you'll learn about the philosophy of Ayurveda and how it has evolved from an ancient, rustic medicine into a staple of the contemporary Indian household. Chapter 2 introduces the basic principles of Ayurvedic nutrition. With this knowledge, you'll be able to understand how the digestive process works and why foods with specific healing qualities are used to prepare meals in each season. Adopting these principles, you'll be able to make smart choices at home, in the supermarket, and at restaurants. Chapter 3 offers information on the tools and equipment that are necessary for your healing kitchen.

Part II is the workhorse section of the book. Chapter 4 provides basic dos and don'ts vis-à-vis Ayurvedic nutrition. Chapter 5 provides basic Ayurvedic recipes. Chapters 6 offers a range of Indo-Western Ayurvedic recipes grouped according to seasonal foods available as per the six different seasons of Ayurveda. Each season contains about ten to twenty recipes that are grouped into about five to six meal plans. Each recipe includes a note indicating the aspect of digestion or health targeted, and how it can be tailored to suit different palates.

Finally, Part III provides a list of resources that will serve as a shopping guide. This will include shops, farms and online companies that provide various herbs, ingredients and the freshest of foods.

The Ayurvedic Diet is not only an introduction to Ayurveda, it can serve as a tool for changing your life for the better by restoring a sense of balance that is so often missing from your frenzied existence. The recipes in this book are meant to help you achieve your ideal weight and proportions, understand your personal wellness blueprint and develop a year-round healthy eating habit that will enable you to always work towards your eudaimonic archetype. They will allow you to harness the benefits of Ayurveda in a completely modern context.

PART I

The Ayurvedic Way of Life

1

A Cultural History of
Ayurvedic Cuisine

WHAT IS AYURVEDA?

If you were born and brought up in India, then you probably assume you know whatever there is to know about Ayurveda, or at least some of it. However, truth be told, what most Indians do know is that this is an old life science, something to do with health and wellness, with terminology that has been bandied about the household for way too long; so long that its true meaning seems to have gotten lost in the mists of time.

Very few of us can actually define Ayurveda in its truest form: a holistic lifestyle medicine that originated in ancient India nearly 5000 years ago. The word itself is Sanskrit for 'the Science (*veda*) of Life (*ayur*)', and this traditional system of healing encompasses just about every aspect of lifestyle: diet, self-care, herbal therapy, bodywork, yoga, meditation, prayer and environment.

The stories of its origins are a dime a dozen, after all we Indians thrive on storytelling, don't we? But here's the one I like the most: tradition has it that the knowledge of Ayurvedic medicine was passed on from the Vedic Gods to a group of mystics who tried to discover the secrets of longevity and the cures for illnesses. Through a series of meditations, they received knowledge ranging from everyday well-being to internal medicine and surgery. The science of Ayurveda remained a verbal tradition in India for hundreds of years until it was compiled into three basic books called the *Charak Samhita* (which talks about internal medicine), the *Sushruta Samhita* (discusses surgery) and the *Ashtanga Hridayam* (a derivative collection that draws from the previous two). That said, apart from these three main academic books so to speak, other lesser-known household manuscripts about the medicine also exist in various local languages and dialects. Thousands of colloquial manuscripts have been passed down from generation to generation within households over the ages. In fact, the last few years have been ripe with controversy as eminent 'Ayurvedic pharma' companies have attempted to lay their hands on manuscripts that have historically been the prized possessions of Indian ménages.

Alas, many such manuscripts have been lost over time. The teachings in these books, recorded in ancient Sanskrit verse, articulate Ayurvedic philosophies and concepts, which sometimes get lost in translation to English or other languages. During the time that India was a colony of the British Empire, the authorities tried to stop the practice of Ayurveda (amongst other traditional medicines) and significantly diminished its popularity. Nevertheless, after India became an independent nation in 1947 Ayurveda underwent a renaissance in which it steadily re-established itself both in India and abroad.

Simply speaking, Ayurveda tells us that the mind and body are not two separate entities, but are in fact a unique psycho-physiological system with intricately related influences. We all look different, behave differently and have different reactions to emotional and physical influences. And while similarities exist between one person and the next, Ayurveda perceives each person as an individual entity, and teaches us that there is no universal solution for any health problem.

Makes perfect sense, doesn't it? Think about how stress affects you and how differently your friends and siblings react to the same situation. You could find that you sleep too little because your sleep patterns have been disrupted by anxiety, but your sister on the other hand may find that she deals with stress by oversleeping. You and I could both have allergies, but mine manifest as headaches whereas you routinely break out in zits. Bottom line, we each have unique ways of manifesting illness and therefore, we need to adopt individual self-care patterns that bring us closest to our natural blueprint or state assuming everything is happy, healthy and normal. True health can only be defined by our ability to live closest to our natural prototype.

In Ayurveda, we talk about living in balance. However, unlike other contemporary definitions of the word, 'balance' does not indicate a state of all things being 'equal'. Rather, once you have understood your own natural blueprint, 'balance' can be understood as keeping it in equilibrium both with its innate physical and emotional tendencies, and the external influences. But of course that's not so easy. The inconsistencies of daily life and living challenge our ability to live as per our natural state and constantly push us away from our natural blueprint into a state of disequilibrium. Ayurveda is the perfect balancer because it addresses the whole person, not just the physical body or the mind, and it does this through lifestyle techniques. Ayurveda's primary focus is on staying healthy and balanced, rather than losing itself in cures that only address the symptoms and not the cause of imbalance.

So taking the mind-body as a single unit rather than two distinct entities, it is palpably obvious that the emotional and physical aspects of disease are intricately connected. Again, this makes perfect sense. After all, if you have a fever, you don't exactly feel happy, do you? When it comes to allopathic treatment and Western medicine, a mental health practitioner can diagnose and treat an illness of the mind while a physician treats the physical body, without there being any connection between the two. Add to this the fact that allopathic medicine, entirely based upon prognosis and cure, does not recognize the power of healing through food. An illness must be identified first to apply treatment. Western medicine does not concern itself with keeping the mind-body healthy and balanced over the long term to prevent illnesses from happening in the first place.

Ayurveda however, takes a completely different stand. As a preventive medicine, it addresses the well-being of the mind-body from within rather than merely addressing the external symptoms of disease. It starts with the basic premise that in order to be healthy, the mind-body must be in a state of balance and that the individual requires an intuitive understanding of oneself to stay that way. And when external influences propel you into a state of ill health, you can apply guided therapeutic measures over the short term to bring the mind-body back into a state of balance and stay that way over the long term. Perhaps the best part of it is that Ayurveda addresses healing through food. What we eat and how we eat it are directly responsible for health and longevity. Fancy that!

As modern medicine strives to integrate with traditional global medicines, the world has begun to become more and more intrigued by Ayurveda. However, the intrigue is unfortunately laced with a series of misconceptions. For example, Ayurveda isn't folklore for the Indian people or a cult form steeped in Hindu worship. Neither is it something to be confused with Unani, homeopathy or Siddha. Rather it is a holistic lifestyle therapy born out of ancient Vedic wisdom that helps address all aspects of emotional and physical well-being. The understanding of the universe is broken down to its basic elements. The mind-body is comprised of these same elements and is, therefore, considered a subset of the universe. Health is directly proportional to the mind-body's alignment with its natural state and our ability to live in harmony with our environs. The Ayurvedic doctor serves as a guide to you, the patient, to help you achieve an intuitive understanding of your own mind-body.

HOW DOES AYURVEDA HEAL THROUGH FOOD?

No doubt you've heard of a variety of forms in Ayurvedic therapy – nasty tasting arishtas or oil-heavy abhyanga techniques from Kerala. Although all that is true, it is a mere fraction of the overall therapy. The good news is that *ahara*, or diet, forms the primary therapy in Ayurveda – both on a preventive and a curative basis. According to ancient medicine, everything that you eat, and the manner in which you eat it, has a strong effect on your mind and body. Therefore, it's not just the food and herbs that you eat, but the amount you eat, the timing of your meals and snacks, and the combinations of flavours, all of which influence your well-being.

In fact, your entire 'eating lifestyle or pattern' can have a therapeutic effect. When you eat well, you maximize your ojas or life-essence – the thing that is responsible for keeping you functioning at optimum levels each day. At any point ojas can be depleted causing you to be worn out, sluggish and resistant to meet the challenges of each new day; or it can be maximized, which means you are vital and in the pink of health, and ready to take on the challenges of each day. To maximize ojas, Ayurveda recommends whole, nutritious foods and eating patterns that are designed to balance your mind-body constitution.

Low ojas is a function of poor digestion stemming from an unbalanced diet. It's one of the first signs of ill health. Indigestion disturbs the health of your constitution at its core, in the gastro-intestinal tract. When your diet is out of balance, not only are food nutrients not easily absorbed, but they can also accumulate as toxins. Many of us tend to take things like burping and gas lightly but truth be told, these are all basic signs of indigestion that must be taken note of as soon as they arise. And ever wonder why your mother was so fixated on your pooping habits as a kid? Because Ayurvedically speaking, poop is your tell-all sign of health. We all feel the effects of poor digestion differently: in the upper digestive tract (i.e., the stomach upwards), in the mid-digestive tract (more or less the small intestines), or in the lower digestive tract (the colon downwards) – and how can you tell? By examining your poop.

How healthy is your poop?

Looking out for your poop is not a project that was supposed to begin and end with your mother. Your poop is the #1 indicator of your health, so examining it closely is a must on any given day.

Is your poop dry or broken up into pieces resembling rabbit turds? This is an indication of excess dryness in your system.

Are you prone to explosive pooping or diarrhoea? This is an indication of excess heat in your body.

Is your poop large, slow, difficult to pass and perhaps laced with mucous? This means that you have probably been eating heavy foods that are clogging up your digestive system and causing overall sluggishness.

All these are indications of poor digestive habits that can lead to depleted levels of ojas causing you to feel out of sorts with the world. Changing your eating habits means that you will soon pass solid, healthy poop that goes in tandem with optimum health and high energy levels.

Since your digestive tract is the site of origin for health imbalances, diet really is the first order of medicine. Now most people tend to think of an Ayurvedic diet as a euphemism for khichadi seven days a week, but that's far from the truth. Eating khichadi is great for certain situations both in wellness and illness, but that's just one small part of it. An Ayurvedic diet can be more general or more specific depending upon the nature of health imbalances. A general, balanced Ayurvedic diet is beneficial for preventing ill health. Not only is this considered to be medicinal in itself, but it also works in tandem with all other aspects of non-dietary Ayurvedic therapy. Specifically tailored diets are prescribed only if diseases exist and is at an advanced stage of disease development.

You must adhere to a specified diet until the intensity of the disease is significantly reduced to support other non-dietary treatment in achieving its healing objective. It is more than likely that as the impact of the disease is reduced, the specific diet will be adjusted too. Specified diets include liquid foods, semi-solids or meals like khichadis that are specially prepared with therapeutic ingredients.

Contrary to popular belief, fasting is not recommended in Ayurveda as it interferes with the normal functioning of your digestive system. However, semi-fasts on liquid diets or lighter foods are often suggested during treatment. What Ayurveda does is it recommends a detox or cleansing diet a couple of times a year. These are loosely termed as 'fasts' and work wonders in helping you to reboot your digestive system. That said they are not to be mistaken for complete abstinence which Ayurvedically speaking is a complete no-no.

Food for any specifically tailored Ayurvedic healing diet is selected bearing in mind health imbalances, their manifestation in the tissues, impaired digestive functioning and also the accumulation of *ama* or toxins. These complaints can also be the result of an improper or unbalanced diet. A made-to-order therapeutic diet is composed of food that is selected to act as a medicine because of its healing quality, taste, post-digestive energizing effects and the compatibility with one's individual state of health.

PRAKRUTI – UNDERSTANDING YOUR UNIQUE MIND-BODY CONSTITUTION

So a healing diet is all very well, but the real question is how then do you custom-make it entirely for yourself? If you know even the tiniest amount about Ayurveda, you'll know that there is no one-size-fits-all policy. The way food affects one person is definitely going to be different from how it affects someone else. On the surface of it, it seems like just a matter of taste – I like bitter and would never dream of putting sugar in my coffee, but you on the other hand, refuse to drink coffee without adding healthy dollops of sugar. But it's actually more than just this – keep in mind that tastes have different impacts on the energy levels of different individuals.

The Ayurvedic concept of *Prakruti*, a Sanskrit word which literally translates into 'nature', refers to your natural mind-body constitution – the unique characteristics that you are born with, perceptible through emotions, behaviour, body type, metabolism and health tendencies. The overall nature of a person's constitution is largely determined by which of the *doshas* (*vata, pitta* or *kapha*)or humours is predominant. All three doshas are responsible for the physiological processes of our mind-body and exist in varying levels in each of us, but the proportions are different. Imagine a pie chart with three sections – although each of these sections are of different sizes for each person, they always add up to 100 per cent.

While it is impossible to define Ayurveda in exact terms, the truth is that most of us have mind-body constitutions dominated by more of one dosha than the other two. This means that our emotional capacities, physical characteristics and behavioural patterns will mostly reflect the qualities of the dominant dosha. Some of us exhibit more than one of the dosha characteristics, in that two of the three doshas exist more or less equally in a higher proportion relative to the third. These are 'mixed dosha' types. It's fairly common, for example, to be a vata-pitta type, exhibiting the physical and emotional characteristics of both doshas – more of one perhaps during a particular season of the year and more of the other during another season.

In other cases, one dosha might dominate physical traits and another dosha shows itself in emotional traits, or both characteristics could be a mix of both doshas. Very few people will actually have equal proportions of all three doshas, making them 'tri-dosha' type, although that's typically the most common choice when doing a self-guided dosha quiz.

Eating according to the Ayurvedic diet means identifying the one predominant dosha that characterizes your mind and body, and planning your meals to keep that dosha in balance.

To increase ojas, your core energy, you need to constantly balance your prakruti, your essential nature. Therefore, understanding your prakruti and the elements that compose it becomes the natural first step in your Ayurvedic diet. Even though you are born with a basic prakruti that is unique and will stay constant throughout your life, the day-to-day interplay of dosha tendencies are likely to vary based upon influences from food, lifestyle, environment and seasons. You must examine your food intake patterns to check whether you are 'eating right' to maintain balance, or whether force of habit – junk foods or meals-on-the-go – are driving any of your doshas into excess. That is exactly what triggers ill health.

How? For the simple reason that as prakruti varies from person to person, so does the definition of balance. In Ayurveda, balance does not mean 'all things being equal', or all of us having equal amounts of each dosha within us. Instead, it is a state of equilibrium wherein our current dosha levels match the specific proportions of our natural mind-body makeup. When in equilibrium, the doshas help us to be our best selves. However, when they go out of balance, they create problems such as sluggishness, dehydration, inflammation and other sensitivities. If you consider that dosha literally translates from Sanskrit as 'that which easily goes off balance', it becomes clear that stasis is a challenge for us all.

If you are like most people then at this point you might wonder which of the doshas is the best. The simple answer is none, and all. What's important to remember is that all three doshas are present in all of us – they have to be as each carries a specific function. However, ideally they are all at their best when they are balanced. No matter what your dominant dosha is, your goal is to bring it into balance and live closest to prakruti, your natural design for perfect health.

WHAT ARE THE THREE DOSHAS?

Vata

Vata is responsible for movement in the mind-body – gross motor force, fine motor force, movement of food down your GI tract, physical transportation, movement of thoughts in your mind or nervous impulses and so on. The characteristics of vata (air and space) can be likened to those in a desert – a vast amount of space with air moving through it. Unobstructed, the air can change its course with complete freedom and flexibility. People with a vata-dominant prakruti are creative and free-spirited. They have amazing thinking power and perhaps a bent towards spirituality. They make talented artists, composers, writers or scientists. Physically, vata dosha types tend to be small-boned, with a tendency towards dry, thin, translucent skin, dry hair, cold extremities and erratic eating patterns, behaviour and habits. They have a hard time sitting still.

Pitta

Pitta is responsible for absorption and transformation in the mind-body – thought process, actual digestive changes of state, enzymatic activity, metabolism, hormonal activity and so on. The pitta constitution (fire and water) is like a volcano – it has a liquid heat smouldering deep inside, which sometimes gushes out with dynamic intensity and drive. People with a pitta-dominant prakruti are intense, organized and execution-oriented, with a fantastic sense of purpose. They can process thoughts in a logical manner and make excellent leaders, managers or mathematicians. Physically, the pitta types tend to have oily skin and hair with a 'patchy' quality to it (this can mean an uneven skin tone, combination skin that is more oily in the T-zone (the forehead and nose area), thinner hair and/or a certain flush to the skin). Their hair and skin react easily to hormonal sensitivity and they are generally more prone to feeling hot and irritable.

Kapha

Kapha is responsible for lubrication, structure and binding in the mind-body. The soothing and stable qualities of kapha (water and earth) resemble those of clay – sand and water – coming together to form something that can take shape and create vessels that have holding power without being unduly disturbed. People with a kapha-dominated prakruti are nurturing, compassionate, meticulous and have a wonderful ability to put physical structure to ideas and plans. These people make great health-care workers, caregivers or workers in any occupation that requires persistence, physical stamina and precision. Physically, they are heavier, stable people with skin that is cool and moist to the touch, thick hair all over the body and thicker, spongier skin. Kapha dosha types tend to feel cold and break out into cool, clammy perspiration. The kapha dosha is synonymous with bounty and abundance, especially that which lasts a long time.

Doshas through life

Each dosha is a type of energy that exists in the world around us, and each of these energies has a special influence on us during the different stages of our lives. During childhood and youth, for example, kapha enhances chubbiness, so a plump baby is considered to have strong ojas. From puberty to menopause, pitta increases acidity and heat in the body, giving us the strength to carry ourselves through those changes. Good stamina, leadership and forbearance in transitional periods are all examples of strong ojas during the pitta phase of our lives. Later in life, vata holds sway, bringing with it the lines of age, drier skin and sleep challenges. But this is also the time in life when our spiritual abilities are at their highest potential. Wisdom and spirituality are examples of strong ojas during this life stage. Again, this basic knowledge will naturally impact your food choices at different stages of your life.

DOSHAS OUT OF BALANCE

When doshas go askew or become excessed, you experience low ojas. Imbalances (vikruti) refer to an excess or accumulation of any one or more of the doshas, causing negative forces and toxins to begin spreading through the body. Minor disparities of vata, pitta or kapha are often manifested as dryness, a general sensation of heat and heaviness in the mind and body. You could become intolerant of foods with similar dosha qualities as your predominant dosha. Left unattended, these imbalances can develop into illnesses, therefore it is important to be aware of their symptoms.

The pressures of modern life wreak havoc with our doshas. In ancient times, people modelled their lifestyle on nature and the seasons. Today, environmental influences like light, heat and water that once ruled our work and sleep patterns fall easily under our control. Conveniences like eating seasonal fruits year round, driving instead of walking, and unhealthy diet and exercise habits distract us from our natural life rhythms. The net result is that it's easy to find yourself run down, stressed out and feeling at odds with the world because your doshas are out of sync. Ayurveda recognizes the need to rejuvenate from within by setting the dosha composition back to prakruti, its natural starting point. This doesn't mean reverting to the ways of your ancestors, but rather learning from their wisdom to gently tweak your own lifestyle to bring you back into balance.

Your predominant dosha is understandably the one most likely to become imbalanced. For example, vata folks who are out of balance might have lower immunity and a tendency to catch colds on a regular basis. Each dosha expresses imbalance in a different way. Learning to read these signs will help you regain your alignment quickly.

Vata is the most volatile of the three doshas. Too much vata energy creates dryness in the colon causing pain, fatigue and lowered immunity. It manifests as anxiety, the inability to focus and fear. Vata imbalances tend to make you 'spacey', absent-minded and causes you to behave erratically. Dryness and low skin elasticity begin to manifest as wrinkles. Your nerves might be frayed and your sleep patterns disturbed.

Pitta imbalances raise heat in the mid-digestive tract. Too much pitta energy manifests itself emotionally as anger, intolerance and criticism; or physically as acidity, inflammation and allergies. People with pitta imbalances are prone to acne, heat toxins, any kind of 'itis', food and cosmetics sensitivities, dust and pollen allergies.

Kapha imbalances secrete excess juices in the upper digestive tract, causing sluggishness, depression, water retention, fat and excessive mucus. Too much kapha energy can lead to clogged pores and follicles, congested skin, 'couch-potato' behaviour and eating for comfort.

DHAATUS – OUR PHYSICAL TISSUES FORMED FROM THE DIGESTIVE PROCESS

While the doshas are responsible for the physiological processes of the mind-body – movement, transformation and lubrication – there are seven tissue layers or dhaatus that are the main physical constituents of the body.

You might be wondering why Ayurvedic doctors are so focused on perfect digestion. Essentially, it boils down to the fact that the dhaatus of the physical body are formed from the digestive process: *Rasa* (plasma), *Rakta* (blood), *Mamsa* (muscle and connective tissue), *Meda* (fat), *Asthi* (bone), *Majja* (nerve) and *Shukra* (reproductive).

After digestion, food takes primarily two forms – prasada or essence and kitta or refuse. Prasada provides nourishment to the seven dhaatus, building each one successively from the last. And kitta nourishes vata, pitta, kapha, hair, nails, stool, sweat, excreta of eyes, ears, nose, mouth and genital organs.

Here's how this works:

Each dhaatu has its own *agni* or 'digestive fire' which initiates a process of transformation. The product of this dhaatu-agni process feeds the next layer of tissue. So rasa dhaatu, the first layer of tissue, is directly fed by the agni from the digestive process. Then rakta dhaatu, the second tissue layer, is formed from the dhaatu-agni process of the rasa dhaatu. After this, the dhaatu-agni of rakta feeds mamsa. And so on until the tissue layer is formed successively to the last dhaatu.

Ojas is the supreme essence distilled from all seven dhaatus, beginning with rasa and ending in shukra, that determines the quality of your physical, mental and spiritual endurance. An insufficiency or an overabundance of any dhaatu will negatively impact ojas which in turn leads to an increase in the ama produced by the body, thereby hampering your physical and mental capacity.

It makes sense then as to why the digestive process is so critical to maximizing ojas.

Besides feeding the next layer of tissue, the dhaatu-agni process forms secondary tissues or *updhaatus* as well as by-products of kitta or waste known as *kittapaka*.

Therefore, not only does the quality of the dhaatu-agni process of each tissue layer determine the development of the next tissue layer, it also determines the quality of the secondary tissue and waste including the doshas. Since the dhaatus support and are nourished by each other, affecting any one can influence another. So if an over or under development of any particular dhaatu is bound to influence the development of the subsequent layers, both may hinder nutrition. These then become basic indicators for assessing tissue health.

As the dhaatus are also governed by the three doshas, any imbalance in the doshas is bound to cause imbalances in the dhaatus.

Dhaatu	Element	Updhaatu	Kittapaka	Health indications
Rasa	Water	Breast milk, menstrual flow	Kapha plegm	Well hydrated, soft and oily skin, uniform complexion, deep-rooted hair, lustrous skin and hair
Rakta	Fire	Blood vessels, fascia	Pitta bile	Good complexion, energetic, happy, cheerful, delicate, low sun-tolerance, rosy-pink lips, cheeks, tongue, conjunctiva, nails, ears and genitalia
Mamsa	Earth, water, fire, air	Ligaments, skin	Ear wax, nose crust	Muscular build, stability, endurance, strong neck, well-toned and defined muscles on the face, cheeks, chest, abdomen, arms and legs
Meda	Water, earth	Lymphatic vessels, tendons	Sweat	Optimal fatty tissue under the skin, shiny hair and nails, oily faces, soft and smooth complexion, melodious voice, appropriate sweating, well-lubricated joints, optimum body bulk, compassionate
Asthi	Earth, air	Teeth	Nails, hair	Strong bones and teeth, plenty of healthy hair, strong nails, tall, robust, good stamina, hardworking, strong and sturdy look

Dhaatu	Element	Updhaatu	Kittapaka	Health indications
Majja	Water, earth	Hair	Tears, eye secretions	Strong nervous system, soft and unctuous complexion, big, bright and attractive eyes, intelligent, soft organs, well-oiled joints, good memory
Shukra	Essence	Ojas	Waste material from the genitals	Good sex drive and endurance, gentle, loving appearance, attractive, cheerful, well-developed buttocks

Sixteen physical and non-physical *srotas* or channels then transport the doshas' nutrition, waste, thought and energy to other parts of the mind-body. Toxic build-up or *ama* can block srota functioning, leading to disease.

Finally, three principal *malas* or waste materials emanate from the digestive process: *purisha* (faeces), *mutra* (urine) and *sveda* (sweat). Too little or too much of each of these is an indicator of ill-health.

One important thing to note here: each stage of dhaatu formation takes about five days which means that it takes about thirty-five days in total to produce ojas from the initial point of food consumption. So changing your lifestyle to incorporate the Ayurvedic diet means that it will take at least this much time before you begin to see a perceptible difference. As I mentioned in the introduction, the first few weeks might not be easy, but that is because you have pushed the reset button and your body is taking time to re-adjust. Stick with it! In a few weeks you'll feel like you are on top of the world.

The Dosha Quiz – Understanding What Doshas Dominate Your Prakruti

While an Ayurvedic doctor or practitioner can most accurately determine your prakruti, here is a simple quiz that will help give you a sense of your primary dosha, the building block of your dietary routine.

For each question, choose as many answers you feel apply to you. All your answers do not have to be from the same dosha type. Rather than trying to answer based on how you feel right now, or want to look and feel, think specifically about how you usually look and feel. Whichever dosha you answer with the most often is your predominant dosha. Keep this dosha in mind as you read about the routines for personal care, yoga and diet in the following chapters. While each of the doshas can go out of balance at any time, it is your dominant dosha that best predicts how you naturally feel. Over time, you can repeat this quiz to see what your dominant dosha is in different phases of your life.

An electronic version of this quiz is also available at www.reenita.com/doshaquiz.

The skin on my face is ...

vata   normal to dry. I have a tendency towards fine lines and wrinkles. My skin lacks muscle tone or elasticity. It feels dry or tight when I travel, get dehydrated or go out in cold weather.

pitta   oily on the T-zone and dry on the cheeks. My skin tends to be sensitive and might redden or break out when exposed to chemicals, cosmetics, soap and synthetics. I might have moles, freckles or hyper-pigmentation.

kapha   normal to oily. My skin tone is quite supple and elastic, although my face might get puffy. I have a tendency to have large pores and sometimes get whiteheads and pustules.

The skin on my body is ...

vata   normal to dry. It is thin and translucent, so you can often see my veins through the skin. It can lack elasticity and sag in some places. It might be rough or flakes easily in certain areas.

pitta   normal to sensitive. It has warmth and a flush to it and reddens easily, especially in the sun or warmer weather. I might scar easily or have hyper-pigmentation marks. I may scratch my skin in response to sensitivities, which then causes the skin to scar.

kapha   normal, thick and spongy. It has a good, strong, supple tone and elasticity. My skin might retain water from time to time.

The temperature of my skin is ...

vata   cool or cold. I have cold hands and feet, and I usually feel cold, especially in dry climates.

pitta   warm. My skin is warm to the touch, especially in the upper torso, and my hands, feet, groin and underarms tend to perspire. I feel hot and sweaty fairly readily, especially in warmer weather. My perspiration can have an offensive odour.

kapha   cold. My skin might feel cool to the touch even in fatty areas such as the buttocks, hips, thighs or upper arms. It does not breathe well in cool, damp climates, and my pores tend to become clogged with oil. I often experience a cool 'clammy-all-over' kind of perspiration.

My body frame is ...

vata   small, lean, or wiry, either tall and thin or small and petite. I have lighter and less dense bones.

| pitta | compact, athletic and muscular. I have a medium build and a well-defined musculature and bone structure. |
| kapha | large. I have wide hips and shoulders. I have large muscles, and dense and heavy bones. |

My body frame has ...

vata	less amounts of fat right under the skin. I can lose (or gain) weight quickly and can get 'scrawny' at times.
pitta	a medium layer of fat right under the skin (more in some areas and less in others). I have a good, strong metabolism and can gain or lose weight relatively easily.
kapha	a thick layer of fat under the skin. I can gain weight easily, and find it relatively hard to lose it.

Without chemical treatments, the texture of my hair is ...

vata	wavy, dry, with a flyaway tendency. My scalp tends to be dry and may flake when rubbed. I sometimes have dandruff.
pitta	fine, oilier in patches. My scalp can be sensitive to chemicals in hair products and prone to dandruff.
kapha	lustrous, beautiful, with a natural shine and moisture. My scalp can be slightly oily to the touch. Sometimes the oil can clump up, forming large, oily dandruff.

The strength and thickness of my hair is ...

vata	inconsistent. While each individual hair might be thin and relatively dry or brittle, I have a lot of hair on my head.
pitta	fine. Each individual hair is fine and the overall volume is thin and can even seem scanty. I am prone to premature hair loss or greying hair.
kapha	thick. Each individual hair is strong, thick and resistant to damage. I have lots of hair on my head.

My nails are ...

vata normal to dry. They break easily and are better managed if kept short. They might have ridges.

pitta pinkish and fairly strong.

kapha big and thick with prominent white moons. They are strong and resistant to damage.

My eyes are ...

vata small with sparse lashes. They get dry easily.

pitta sharp and clear. They are sensitive to bright light and redden easily with external influences like dust, pollen, cosmetics, strong light or foods that do not agree with me.

kapha large and picturesque, perhaps even dreamy. They might get puffy or have some whitish discharge from time to time.

My digestion is ...

vata irregular. Sometimes I am hungry at mealtimes and sometimes I am not. I might forget to eat and then feel spacey or weak, or tend towards constipation, gas, bad breath and hard, dry or small, rabbit-like stool.

pitta intense. If I delay eating past my regular mealtimes, I get irritable. I sometimes get loose stools, heartburn or acidity. My stool can be 'explosive'.

kapha consistent or low. I can go without a meal if I am still full from the last one, but I also tend to eat for comfort. I often have a slower passage of thick, well-formed stools, perhaps lined with mucous. I might even go a day or two between stools.

My sleep patterns are ...

vata light and interrupted. I might stay awake for part of the night or have fitful, interrupted sleep. I usually cannot remember my dreams, but when I do, they tend to be vivid or imaginative.

pitta   regular. I sleep about the same number of hours and feel rested. I have active dreams, sometimes even violent ones.

kapha   deep and heavy. I sleep long hours. I am not a morning person.

Emotionally speaking, I am ...

vata   quick-minded and imaginative. I am perceptive, excitable and can get restless with creativity. I am friendly and exuberant.

pitta   an organized and disciplined person. I am usually quite intense and passionate about what I do.

kapha   calm, steady and nurturing. I do not get easily influenced or excited. I am a loyal, loving friend.

Intellectually speaking, I am ...

vata   all over the place. I sometimes find it difficult to focus because I get excited about things. I tend to have a short memory.

pitta   sharp, analytical, intelligent and focused. I have a good memory, and good management and leadership skills.

kapha   a slow learner. I learn by doing and repetition. I have a long-term memory.

When I manifest emotional imbalance, I ...

vata   become anxious, nervous or fearful. I might get spacey or find it hard to focus when I am stressed.

pitta   become critical, controlling and angry. I range from being irritable to completely volatile when I am stressed.

kapha   become stubborn and stuck-in-the-mud, I hold things in, 'shut down' and become impossible to communicate with when I am stressed.

The pace of my life is ...

vata   intentionally fast. I keep myself busy to stay happy and prevent boredom.

pitta   intense. My activities are well laid-out and organized, but require my absolute focus and involvement.

kapha   slow. I like to follow through my personal projects at my own pace.

2

Understanding How Digestion Works

To understand the Ayurvedic digestive process, it is essential to understand the concepts of *agni* or digestive fire, *guna* or energetic healing quality of food and the theory of taste and post-digestive energetic effects of food. I have explained these in some detail here.

AGNI – THE AYURVEDIC CONCEPT OF 'DIGESTIVE FIRE'

I've already touched up on the concept of agni in explaining the dhaatu formation process, but to truly understand Ayurvedic digestion, it is critical to understand the role of agni in the digestive process.

Agni translates from Sanskrit as 'fire'. Unlike its literal meaning, agni represents 'digestive fire' – a key concept in Ayurvedic health. Agni describes the forces used to break down the substances that you consume on a daily basis and utilize their components in the process of metabolism. Such forces exist in the digestive tract as the main agni process, but they also extend to the digestive support organs and other tissues such as 'lesser agnis'. The primary agni in the digestive system includes the gastric juices and enzymes which initiate the digestive process. The lesser agnis encompass the digestive support organs such as the liver, spleen, gall bladder, pancreas and other organs that aid in the absorption of nutrients and the flushing out of toxic waste matter. The lesser agnis also include tissue metabolism or utilizing the nutrients from the digestive process to build up strong and healthy tissue matter.

A metabolic process, rather than a 'physical entity', agni is present in every cell of the living body where the osmotic process of nutrient exchange occurs at the cellular level. Agni maximizes vitality by eliminating toxins and maintaining immunity at all levels of organ and tissue functioning. The natural quality of agni is light and hot. As in all other mind-body processes, balance is essential as a balanced agni is directly proportional to a balance of doshas, a balanced assimilation-metabolism process resulting in a balanced mind-body and maximized ojas. A weakened agni results in hypo-metabolism causing heaviness, debility and the accumulation of undigested food matter leading to ama and toxic accumulation. An overactive agni causes hyper-metabolism leading to excessive sweating, hunger, weakness in the mind-body and a hampered sense of taste and smell. Finally, an erratic agni produces irregular metabolism causing digestive pain, distension, constipation or diarrhoea, fatigue and insecurity. Erratic agni patterns are very prevalent in today's culture, conceived and exacerbated by our 'on-the-go' lifestyle.

Agni changes with age. Gentler in the younger years, it accelerates around puberty and then stabilizes through most of our adult years. It then begins to slow down through the middle years causing the tissues to gradually age and decay from thereon.

GUNA – THE ENERGETIC QUALITY OF FOOD

Different foods have different *gunas* or energetic qualities. For example, cheese is heavy and dense, whereas rye is light and dry. Mint has a cold quality, whereas ghee nourishes the body tissues and provides stability. Such qualities directly affect our mind-body both physically and emotionally. For example, drinking coffee can have a diuretic effect on the physical body, but also stimulates the mind.

The energetic qualities of a food will naturally have an effect on our mind-body. For example eating popcorn which is dry and light in quality, will increase lightness and dryness in the system, making it a popular snack for a heavier set person. On the other hand, eating hot food will help counter the cold in winter. Similarly, Ayurvedic meals vary from season to season with foods and ingredients selected for energetic qualities that balance the energies of the season.

There are twenty gunas in all, the quality of any is impossible to realize without experiencing the opposite guna. They are usually listed in ten pairs.

All foods have an effect on your digestion and your natural body function. There is no golden rule for how much of a particular food quality is good for you. The key is to understand your limits based upon your natural Ayurvedic constitution. So consider these energetic pairings:

Guna Pairings

Hot – cold
Hard – soft
Dry – oily
Light – heavy
Dull – sharp
Gross – subtle
Slimy – rough
Stable – mobile
Turbid – transparent
Solid – liquid

Light/Heavy

Light food like popcorn or salad bring lightness into your constitution, improve physical and emotional agility of the body and mind and boost inspiration. But eating them in excess will leave you undernourished and exhausted.

Heavier foods like meats or wheat are generally more grounding, but eat more than what is good for your constitution and you will notice that you begin to feel nauseous and put on weight.

Hot/Cold

Cruciferous vegetables like asparagus and cauliflower, or herbs like coriander, are cooling whereas others like sweet pepper, chillies and ginger are heating. Just as heating and cooking food makes it more digestible, so do eating foods with the heating quality stimulate digestion and speed up the metabolism. Too much of them can, however, overstimulate your appetite, causing you to eat in excess, giving you heartburn.

Cooling foods on the other hand clarify your mind and refresh your body in warm environments. Cold food is harder to digest, therefore too much of it ends up depressing your immune system.

Dry/Moist

This is a trickier combination to understand – most Ayurvedic texts will simply define this is as dry vs oily. However, there are three distinct types in the dry-moist spectrum.

Dry foods include things like bread or idlis. They bring lightness and agility, however too much of them causes dehydration, leading to stiffness and pain sensitivities.

Moist foods are of two kinds – those with dry moisture, like water or celery which are more moist than dry foods, but less moist than foods with oily moisture, like nuts and oil. Moist foods enhance lubrication, softness in the mind and body, and also boost emotion; oiliness enhances our ability to connect. Too much moisture or oiliness however gives rise to over-emotional behaviour and clinginess. We all tend to have more moisture in our mind-body when we are younger, but this dissipates as we grow older, hence the need to replenish moisture from the food we eat.

Solid/Liquid

Solid food is that which you need to masticate to a liquid state before swallowing like, rice with vegetables. Liquid food however, such as soup or dal, is food that you can readily swallow. Then there is semi-solid food like khichadi and porridge. Solid food is more dehydrating as it utilizes gastric juices for digestion; liquid food on the other hand is typically moist and oily. Solid food provides solidity and structure but if taken in excess, digesting it can lead to exhaustion.

Liquid food keeps the body hydrated and is easily digestible, but too much of it depletes the structure and can negatively impact your immune system.

Dull/Sharp

Sharp foods like certain spices produce their effect quickly and therefore stimulate. In excess however, they can overstimulate or irritate.

Dull foods like cakes taste good, but too much will slow digestion and clog the intestines.

Stable/Mobile

Stable foods like coconut oil have strong chemical bonds that are not easily broken so the properties of the food do not change. Coconut oil does not break down in the cooking process, therefore, it is good fat to use for cooking. Stable foods provide balance.

Mobile foods like alcohol move quickly through your system and are absorbed into your tissues, but you need to be careful about not taking them in excess as they can be severely toxic and can lead to free radical formation.

Hard/Soft

Mineral rich foods like salt or bananas stabilize and strengthen the body but in excess, they could cause rigidity.

Soft foods like fruits bring satisfaction and relaxation. Too much softness however leads to a passive state.

Turbid/Transparent

Clear, transparent food is fresh, pure and boosts mental clarity. Too much however can leave you restless.

Turbid foods can indicate fermentation. This can stimulate digestion, but can also be tamasic.

Slimy/Rough

Rough foods like raw vegetables need to be well masticated before swallowing.

Smooth foods like yoghurt line the tissues, but too much creates mucus. Too much roughness dries up your digestive tract.

Subtle/Gross

These qualities are evident when it comes to the size of food, for example coarsely chopped versus julienned vegetables. Fineness increases subtlety in our observation, but too much subtlety leaves us overstimulated.

Grossness protects the senses, stimulates grounding and has something earthy to it. Too much grossness makes us insensitive.

What's critical to note, however, is that on the face of it, all these qualities are purely objective and looking at them in isolation does not indicate whether the food is good or bad for you. What you need to eat depends entirely upon the season, your natural constitution and whether it is in balance or not. When you go through the year, from season to season, you will find that many of these qualities are heightened in the atmosphere. For example, early winter is characterized by dryness and cold winds. As such, this is the time when your diet should naturally comprise of hydrating foods.

TASTES AND POST-DIGESTIVE TASTES

In Ayurveda there are six different tastes or rasa, each of which relates to two of the five elements, each of which has a unique effect on the mind-body constitution influencing the way we feel and how much energy we have. The fire and air elements are light and tend to move upwards. Therefore, rasa containing these elements also move upwards to heat our upper body and provide lightness to the system. The earth and water elements are heavy and move downwards. Therefore, rasa containing these elements cool the lower part of our body and produce heaviness.

Tastes and the Elements	
Tastes	Elements
Sweet (madhur)	Earth + Water
Sour (amla)	Earth + Fire
Salty (lavana)	Water + Fire
Pungent (katu)	Fire + Air
Bitter (tikta)	Air + Space
Astringent (kshaya)	Air + Earth

Each taste has its own specific heating or cooling energy in the mouth and upper digestive tract. For example, sweet tastes have a cooling effect on our minds and particularly help cheer us up when we are upset. Pungent tastes

Elements and Foods	
Elements	*Food Examples*
Earth	Wheat, rice, root vegetables, salts, minerals, seeds
Water	Milk, dairy, juicy fruits, juicy vegetables, salts
Fire	Spices, chillies, sour fruits, alcohol, tobacco
Air	Dried fruits, raw vegetables, nightshades, beans
Space	Narcotics, alcohol, tobacco, caffeine

have a heating effect on the physical body and are particularly helpful in kindling our internal thermostat.

More important than the initial heating or cooling effect is the ultimate energetic effect it has on the mind-body once it has gone through the digestive process. This is not necessarily the same as the initial heating or cooling effect. For example, turmeric has a pungent rasa and a heating *virya*, but its *vipak* or post-digestive energetic effect is actually cooling. Understanding the post-digestive vipak in relation to virya and rasa can be challenging at first, but it is necessary for preparing healing food and for understanding the food's *prabhava* or specific dynamic action on the mind-body.

What Are the Six Tastes and How Do They Relate to Digestion?

Textbook Western nutrition thinks of a balanced meal as one which combines carbohydrates, proteins and fats, but in Ayurveda, we're all about the energetic effects that food has on our mind-body.

A balanced meal is one that comprises all six tastes. Most

foods are a combination of more than one taste. We can then further tailor them to dosha-balancing needs by having more of some tastes than others. A healthy person is able to enjoy all six tastes, but if you have an imbalance, or *vikruti*, then you might develop an aversion to foods with similar qualities as the doshas are imbalanced. These foods are then no longer palatable, no longer medicinal and can even become harmful for you. Therefore, if you have too much fire in your constitution, then foods with spices and chillies will not appeal to you. When you are feeling out of balance, you need to change your diet to help restore balance.

The Six Tastes (Rasa)

[A] Sweet

Foods with a sweet taste are calming and soothing to the system. Their grounding qualities balance vata, and their cooling qualities balance pitta. However, if taken in excess, these foods will imbalance kapha, creating heaviness and slowing digestion. Sweet foods include sugar, honey, milk, sesame seeds, fruits and vegetables with a naturally sweet taste such as bananas, yams or fennel and also carbohydrates such as potatoes, rice or bread.

[B] Bitter

Foods with a bitter taste create lightness and clarity. They balance kapha and pitta, but if taken in excess, they aggravate vata, inducing dryness in the skin. Bitter foods include olives, dark leafy green vegetables like spinach or mustard greens and coffee.

[C] Sour

Foods with a sour taste stimulate digestion. Their warming qualities balance vata, but if taken in excess they will disturb kapha and pitta, increasing body weight and skin sensitivity. Sour foods include yoghurt and sour cream, citrus fruits and tomato or fermented foods such as vinegar and pickles.

[D] Pungent

Foods with a pungent taste decongest the body, increasing digestion. Their drying and heating properties balance kapha, but, if taken in excess, these foods can disturb pitta and vata by creating excess heat and dryness inside the body. Pungent foods include garlic, onions, wasabi and hot spices like ginger, cumin and black pepper.

[E] Salty

Foods with a salty taste are calming and enhance digestion. Their warming qualities balance vata, but if taken in excess, they can disturb kapha and pitta, leading to water retention and inflammation. Salty foods include seaweeds, salted chips and other snack foods and soy sauce.

[F] Astringent

Foods with an astringent taste create lightness. Their cooling properties balance pitta and their drawing properties balance kapha, but if taken in excess these foods can disturb vata leading to dryness and flatulence. Astringent foods include pomegranates, aloe vera, green grapes and chickpeas.

For a meal to be balanced, it is important that you pay attention to the order in which we experience the six tastes.

The six tastes digest in a specific order based on doshas. Both sweet and salty tastes are digested in the stomach, the first part of our digestive tract, by the kapha dosha. They have a sweet energetic effect and move downwards in the system. Therefore, these foods should be eaten first. Sour tastes are digested in the small intestine by the pitta dosha where they ignite the digestive juices. These should be eaten next. Pungent, bitter and astringent tastes are digested in the colon by the vata dosha. They all have a pungent vipak and move upwards in the system to create lightness, and so should be eaten last. In the West, meals are typically served in courses. However, in Ayurvedic cooking, specially prepared portions of food representing each rasa are provided according to the doshas we are aiming to balance.

Any given meal should ideally be representative of all six tastes, but you can tailor one or two items depending upon what energetic effects make sense for you. The question then is, how do you determine what foods with which tastes make more sense for you?

Well, that depends on various factors – the season, your age, your prakruti or natural state and vikruti or anything moving you away from that natural state. Both of the latter are determined by your predominant doshas.

3

The Ayurvedic Eating Plan

So now that you have determined your dosha and understood the ins and outs of the Ayurvedic digestive process, the next order of business is how to actually plan your eating. No rocket science here. The *Ayurvedic Diet* is far from 'restrictive'. Rather, it's an open-ended eating plan that is tailored to meet the needs of your prakruti based upon the foods of the season.

PERSONAL DOSHA – RULES OF THUMB

Different dietary plans have different views on how much you should be eating on any given day. Some say three solid meals, others say five smaller meals. Truth be told, the number of meals you eat will depend entirely upon your prakruti.

Vata types have a higher metabolic rate and as long as they are eating the right foods, they will digest relatively quickly. They also tend to eat faster than other dosha types. Therefore, vata folks can have several smaller meals in a day. An ideal eating plan for a vata type would consist of:

- Small meal – breakfast – between 6–8 a.m.
- Easily digestible mid-morning snack – between 8–10 a.m. (ideally consisting of nuts and fruits)
- Main meal of the day – lunch – between 10 a.m. and 2 p.m.
- Easily digestible afternoon snack – between 2–4 p.m. (ideally consisting of nuts and fruits)
- Small meal – dinner – between 5 p.m. and dusk (prefer to not use the word nightfall as I don't want readers to confuse this with 'later into the night')

Of course, the key is to allow plenty of time in between meals for digestion. Ideally, this should be three to four hours, but that can be tricky if you are going to have mid-morning and mid-afternoon snacks. Therefore, it becomes vital that the snacks consist of easily digestible food like fruits with some nuts if necessary. Do not make the classical Western diet-induced mistake of having snacks like fruits with cheese. Not only is it a bad food combination, but even a little bit of cheese takes a long time to digest.

Pitta types can do with three solid meals a day. The main thing is that they should be eaten consistently at regular times. An ideal pitta eating plan would look like this:

- Small meal – breakfast – around 8 a.m. (or between 6–9 a.m.)
- Main meal of the day – lunch – exactly at noon (or between 10 a.m. and 2 p.m.)
- Small meal – dinner – ideally at 6 p.m. or before dusk

What's important is that the pitta dosha types don't eat late in the night. Typically, by staying up past 10 p.m. they tend to get peckish. This has bad repercussions for this category.

Of the three doshas, kapha folks can probably eat the least as they have the slowest digestion. They should eat one solid meal a day – lunch with two mini meals, breakfast and dinner:

- Small meal – breakfast – around 8 a.m. (or between 6–8 a.m.)
- Main meal of the day – lunch – exactly at noon (or between 11 a.m. and 2 p.m.)
- Small meal – dinner – ideally between 5–6 p.m. or before dusk

Or over time, and certainly as they grow older, they could probably just skip their dinner meal.

SEASONAL DOSHA – RULES OF THUMB

The Indian calendar can be segregated into six short seasons, each of which has different dosha influences. Eating Ayurvedically means eating to counter the dosha influences of each particular season. Here is a chart to help you put this in context.

Seasons	When	Effect on dosha	Tastes recommended	Food/Beverage	Nature of season
Shishir (Late Winter)	Mid-Jan to mid-March	K – mild increase V – normal – mild aggravation P – normal	Sweet, sour, salty	Foods prepared with wheat/gram flour, milk products, sugarcane	Cold/oily strong agni
Vasanta (Spring) (Kapha liquefies due to heat)	Mid-March to mid-May	K – aggravates V – normal P – normal	Bitter, astringent, pungent • Water boiled with dry ginger • Shunthi, Ashwagandha and Pippali Kapha – detox with fruit and veggie juice fast is ideal	Moisture-less • Light and easily digestible food. • Barley, honey, roasted meat, mango juice • Water mixed with honey • Avoid hard-to-digest and cold food, sour, sweet and fatty food. • Astringent, bitter, pungent foods	Hot/oily weakened agni

Seasons	When	Effect on dosha	Tastes recommended	Food/Beverage	Nature of season
Grishma (Summer)	Mid-May to mid-July	V – mild increase K – back to normal P – normal	Sweet Avoid • pungent, sour and salty tastes. • hot foods • alcoholic beverages. • caffeine	Eat room temperature rather than cold foods • Eat sweet, cool, light, unctuous and liquid food • Avoid wine • Boiled rice with meat, corn flour, curd (yoghurt) • Rice, milk, ghee, raisins, coconut water • Drink cold water • Panak Panchsara (syrup prepared with draksha, sugarcane, madhuka, date, kashmarya and parshuka fruits all in equal quantity) cold with cardamom powder.	Hot/dry medium agni – weakening towards the end of summer

Seasons	When	Effect on dosha	Tastes recommended	Food/Beverage	Nature of season
Varsha (Monsoon) seasonal switch	Mid-July to Mid-Sep	V – aggravated P – mild increase K – normal/mild aggravation	Sweet, sour, salty • Avoid foods which are heavy and juicy. • Avoid fruits in excess Pitta detox	Hot • Easily digestible food to be eaten. • Pulses, meat, juice, soups, old grains and mastu (thin water of yoghurt) can be taken in food.	Cold/dry weakened agni
Sharad (Autumn) sudden heat after rain	Mid-Sep to mid-Nov	V – back to normal Pitta – aggravated K – normal	Sweet, bitter, astringent Avoid • yoghurt • heavy meals • alcoholic drinks	Moisture-less not heavy, dry • Sweet, light, cold, bitter foods • Eat easily digestible food like rice, green gram, amla, honey and sugar • Ghee, rice, green gram, mulethi	Hot/sharp medium agni

Seasons	When	Effect on dosha	Tastes recommended	Food/Beverage	Nature of season
Hemanta (Early Winter)	Mid-Nov to mid-Jan	Pitta – back to normal V – normal/obstructed K – normal	Sweet, sour, salty Avoid • light and restricted diet • pungent and astringent foods	Hot • Sweet, sour and salty taste • Wine prepared with jaggery (molasses) can be taken. • Wheat/gram flour products, milk products, sugarcane products and corn/edible oils • Heavier foods • Ghee • Dairy products	Cold/oily/ strong agni

FOOD AND EATING GUIDELINES FOR THE DIFFERENT DOSHAS

Vata

- Sip hot water (with lemon) first thing in the morning
- Eat warm, oily, heavy, moist, nourishing foods
- Eat fruit first thing in the morning and eat cooked foods for dinner
- Eat more portions of sweet, sour, salty, pungent foods
- Avoid astringent, cold and bitter foods
- Avoid raw foods and excessive detox diets

Foods to eat and avoid

Recommended beverages:	Warm drinks, herbal teas, fruit and vegetable juices, almond milk, aloe vera juice, apple cider, apricot, carrot, cherry, grape juice, lemonade, mango, orange, papaya, peach, pineapple, rice milk, sour juices, ajwain tea, fennel tea (saunf), fenugreek tea (methi), ginger tea, lemongrass, liquorice (jeshtimadhu) tea, anantamul, mint, raspberry, rosehips, saffron
Avoid:	Carbonated drinks, cold or iced drinks, coffee, tea, alcohol
Recommended condiments:	Mango chutney, lemon, lime, lime pickle, mango pickle, mustard, scallions, seaweed, sprouts, vinegar,

dashmool, ashwagandha, haritaki, ginger, jeshtimadhu, asafoetida,

Avoid: Black pepper, chili peppers, sprouts, coriander seeds, fenugreek (methi)

Recommended dairy: Butter, ghee, whole milk, lassi, cheese, paneer, cottage cheese, sour cream, yoghurt

Avoid: Ice cream, powdered milk

Recommended fruits: Ripe and sweet – cooked apples, applesauce, avocado, banana, berries, cherries, coconut, dates, figs, grapefruit, grapes, kiwi, lemon, lime, mangoes, melons, oranges, papaya, peaches, pineapple, plums, soaked prunes, pomegranate, soaked raisins, rhubarb, strawberries, tamarind, apricots, peaches, dates

Avoid: Dried fruits, hard apples, pears, cranberries

Recommended grains: Whole grains, amaranth, durham flour, cooked oats, sprouted wheat bread, wheat, white basmati rice, shali, red rice, pasta

Avoid: Barley, buckwheat, rye, corn, millet

Recommended dals, beans, legumes: Lentils – red, mung beans, mung dal, toor dal, urad dal

Avoid: Rajma, rongi, split peas, white beans, black beans

Recommended meats: Beef, buffalo, chicken, duck, eggs, turkey, sea food[*]

Recommended nuts and seeds: Almonds, black walnuts, brazil nuts, cashews, charoli, coconut, filberts, hazelnuts, macadamia nuts, peanuts, pecans, pine nuts, pistachios, walnuts, pumpkin seeds, sunflower seeds, sesame seeds

Avoid: Dry roasted, salted and smoked nuts

Recommended oils: Ghee, olive oil, sesame seed oil, sunflower oil

Recommended spices: Ajvain, anise, asafoetida (hing), basil, bay leaf, black pepper, cardamom, cayenne, cinnamon, clove, coriander, cumin, dill, fennel, fenugreek, garlic, fresh ginger, marjoram, mint, mustard seeds, nutmeg, orange peel, oregano, paprika, parsley, peppermint, pippali, poppy seed, rosemary, saffron, salt (saindhava), savoury, spearmint, star anise, tarragon, thyme, turmeric, vanilla, wintergreen

Recommended sweeteners: Fruit juice concentrates, honey, jaggery

---

[*] Even though I personally recommend a vegetarian diet for reasons that I have already explained and the recipes that follow in this book are all vegetarian in keeping with my recommendations, I have listed these as I fully respect that not everyone is keen on vegetarian diets.

Recommended vegetables:	Root vegetables (rather than leafy greens), avocado, asparagus, beets, carrots, cilantro, cucumber, daikon radish, fennel (anise), garlic, green beans, green chillies, leafy greens, leeks, lettuce, mustard greens, okra, black olives, cooked onions, parsley, parsnip, cooked peas, sweet potato, pumpkin, radish, rutabaga, doodhi taro root, water cress, zucchini, eggplant, olives, sweet potato, spinach
Avoid:	Frozen vegetables, raw vegetables, corn, cabbage, cauliflower, lettuce

Pitta

o   Sip hot water (with lemon) first thing in the morning
o   Eat raw foods as much as possible
o   Eat fruit in the morning and stay vegetarian or avoid red meats
o   Eat more portions of cool, sweet, bitter, juicy foods
o   Avoid acidic, sour, spicy, salty, oily, pungent foods
o   Don't eat after 10 p.m.
o   Flavour your food with cooling herbs and spices

During seasons when the pitta dosha is naturally activated in the environment such as during autumn, consider a juice fast of fruit and bitter vegetables along with a raw food diet taken for each meal, one day per week. Also, regardless of the seasons, pitta-dominated dosha types can continue this fast one day a week all through the year.

Foods to eat and avoid

Recommended beverages:	Almond milk, aloe vera juice, coconut milk, fruit and vegetable juices, water, apple, apricot, berry, cherry, amla juice, neem juice, grape, mango, mixed vegetables, peach, pear, pomegranate, prune juice, rice milk, ginger tea, fennel tea, hibiscus tea, lemon balm and lemongrass tea, liquorice (jeshtimadhu) tea, mint tea, anantamul (sarsaparilla)
Avoid:	Processed orange juice, carbonated drinks, hot drinks, tea, coffee, alcohol
Recommended condiments:	Mint and coriander chutney, coriander leaves, sprouts, long pepper (pippali), cardamom (elaichi), cumin (jeera), dill, fennel (saunf), lemongrass, mint (pudina), rose (gulab), fresh turmeric (haldi)
Avoid:	Black pepper, lime, asafoetida (hing), caraway, clove, garlic, mustard seeds, ginger, nutmeg, onion, basil
Recommended dairy:	Unsalted butter, soft cow or goat cheese, ghee, either cow or goat whole milk, lassi

Avoid:	Sour cream, sour yoghurt, hard cheeses
Recommended fruits (ripe and sweet):	Apples, applesauce, apricots, avocado, sweet berries, coconut, dates, figs, red and purple grapes, mango, melons, oranges, pears, pineapple, plums, pomegranate, prunes, raisins, watermelon, bananas, dates, coconut, lychee
Avoid:	Limes, papaya, apricots, sour cherries, citrus, pineapple
Recommended grains:	Whole grains – amaranth, barley, durham flour, oat bran, oats, pasta, rice cakes, spelt, sprouted wheat bread, wheat, tapioca, white basmati rice
Avoid:	Corn, millet, rye, buckwheat
Recommended legumes:	Green gram, black beans, black-eyed peas, chickpeas (garbanzo beans), kidney beans, brown and red lentils, lima beans, mung beans, mung dal, navy beans, fresh peas, split peas, white beans
Recommended nuts and seeds:	Almonds without skins, charoli, coconut, psyllium, pumpkin, sunflower
Avoid:	Sesame seeds
Recommended oils:	Ghee, sunflower oil, coconut oil, soy
Avoid:	Amonds, corn, sesame, olive, peanuts

Recommended spices:	Sweet basil, tulsi (holy basil), cardamom, cinnamon, coriander, cumin, dill, fennel, mint, peppermint, saffron, spearmint, turmeric, saindhava (rock salt)
Avoid:	Black pepper, caraway, tarragon, vanilla, curry leaves, orange peel
Recommended sweeteners:	Fruit juice, jaggery, honey
Recommended vegetables:	Asparagus, bitter melon, broccoli, brussel sprouts, cabbage, carrots, cauliflower, celery, corn, cilantro, cucumber, fennel (anise), green beans, leafy greens (lettuce), cooked leek, mushrooms, okra, black olives, cooked onions, parsley, parsnip, peas, sweet red peppers, white or sweet potato, prickly pear leaves, pumpkin, squash, sprouts, doodhi, taro root, wheat grass sprouts, zucchini
Avoid:	Radish, watercress, avocado, beets, chillies, carrots, eggplant, olives, raw onions, pickles, tomato, turnip

Kapha

o Sip hot water (with lemon or lime) first thing in the morning and through the day to aid digestion
o Eat raw foods in warmer weather or cooked warm, foods in the cooler weather

- ○ Eat fruit in the morning and less meat or non-vegetarian food through the day
- ○ Eat more portions of dry, light, spicy, heating foods
- ○ Avoid heavy, cold, sweet, sour, gooey or watery foods
- ○ Avoid fatty and deep-fried foods
- ○ Wake up early and exercise

During seasons when the kapha dosha dominates the environment such as late winter and spring, consider a juice fast of fruit or vegetables eaten for each meal one day per week. Kapha dominated dosha types can continue this fast one day a week through the year and combine with juice of bitter greens, celery and carrot or pomegranate juice.

Foods to eat and avoid

Recommended beverages:	Warm drinks, herbal teas, aloe vera juice, apple cider, apricot, berry, spiced black tea, carrot, cherry, cranberry, pomegranate, prune juice, mint tea, ginger tea, hibiscus tea, lemon grass
Avoid:	Apple juice, pineapple juice, tea, alcohol, iced drinks, carbonated drinks
Recommended condiments:	Take more of black pepper, chilli peppers, mint chutney, coriander leaves, horseradish, lemon, mustard, green onions, seaweed and any kind of sprouts, ananthamul, fresh turmeric

Recommended dairy: Cottage cheese, non-fat milk (both from goat's milk), lassi

Avoid: Excess ghee and other dairy products – cheese, kheer, etc.

Recommended fruits: Apples, apricots, berries, cherries, cranberries, pears, peaches, dried fruit, guava, papaya, persimmon, pomegranate, prunes, raisins, amla

Avoid: Dried or fresh figs, grapes, strawberries, bananas, citrus, dates, coconuts, mango, melon, pineapple, plums, rhubarb

Recommended grains: Whole grains barley, buckwheat, dry or puffed cereals, corn, rye, millet, white rice (basmati only), spelt, sprouted wheat bread – Essene, tapioca, wheat bran, fast-growing rice (shastika), a type of red rice (shali), beans/lentils

Avoid: Oats, rice (other than the ones mentioned above), wheat, pasta

Recommended beans, dals, legumes: Black beans, black-eyed peas (rongi), red and brown lentils, lima beans, peas, split peas, toor dal, white beans, mung

Avoid: Rajma, channa

Recommended meats: If you must, then stick to white meats – chicken, eggs, fish, turkey

Recommended nuts and seeds:	Sunflower, pumpkin seeds, almonds, popcorn
Avoid:	Sesame seeds and other nuts
Recommended oils:	Corn, sunflower, olive oil, mustard oil
Recommended spices:	All spices are okay, however not excess salt
Recommended sweeteners:	Avoid sweeteners, but if you must then use fruit juice, honey
Recommended vegetables:	Asparagus, beet greens, beets, bitter melon, broccoli, cabbage, carrots, cauliflower, celery, cilantro, corn, radish, dandelion greens, eggplant, fennel (anise), garlic, green beans, green chillis, horseradish, kale, leafy greens like lettuce, green onions, mushroom, mustard greens, okra, onions, parsley, peas – especially dried, sweet and hot peppers, prickly pear, white potato, radish, spinach, sprouts, squash, summer tomatoes – cooked, turnip greens, turnips, watercress, wheat grass
Avoid:	Sweet potatoes, pumpkin, doodhi

4

Basic Dos and Don'ts of Ayurvedic Nutrition

Most people think of Ayurveda as some fuddy-duddy, hard-to-follow, ancient dietary regimen preached by your grandmother. And while it's true that she probably did preach it, the system is far from what you may think. In fact, it makes perfect sense. Wisdom from previous generations is probably our greatest legacy and unfortunately, as we have so-called 'evolved', over the years we've lost way too much of that basic wisdom that was historically passed down from generation to generation.

To put this in context, here are some key facts about the Ayurvedic diet that are fairly elementary, but many people aren't aware of because they somehow got lost along the way:

1. Fresh foods is what it's all about

Consider this – if you eat an apple at peak freshness, it tastes good and chances are that it'll make you feel great too. But are you going to eat an apple that's soft and wilted? First off, it'll taste bad and second, it's not going to do anything great for your health, is it? I can't stress enough how much Ayurveda insists upon fresh food. Food that is stale starts going bad not just outside its packaging, but also inside your body, releasing toxins into the digestive system which are then absorbed by your other bodily systems too.

Were you aware of this already? Then why is it that I am ready to bet that you resort to ready, prepared meals or preservative loaded packaged foods at least a few, if not several, times a week?

Low quality foods such as canned, processed, spoilt, refrigerated and genetically engineered foods, alcohol, tobacco and narcotics are known as *tamasic* foods or those that create resistance to the mind-body's normal course of action. These foods should be completely eschewed at some stage of life as they cause physical and mental dysfunction over short and long terms. Frozen or refrigerated meals, and food prepared with preservatives and chemicals are a recent Western import that strays far from Ayurvedic nutritional health philosophies. How many times have you seen or heard your grandmother prepare fresh breakfast, lunch or dinner? That's because in Ayurveda, we don't have any concept of leftovers – stale food is tamasic. It starts rotting barely a few hours after it has been prepared and no amount of refrigeration is going to change that. So why would you keep rotting food in the fridge, much less lace your insides with it days later?

This is a good segue into talking about vegetarian foods as well. Ayurveda in itself is not vegetarian philosophy, but you have to remember that the way we live today is a lot different from the hunter-gatherer lifestyles of our ancestors. Basically, when it comes to animal-fare, it must be eaten fresh – back in the day, this is what your ancestors did. They'd go out, hunt an animal, kill it, skin it, cook it and eat it. Not store it in a freezer for the next month!

Think about it, the moment an animal is killed, its flesh begins to rot. So chances are that what you purchase from your grocery store is already well into the rotting phase. And once in your fridge, it just rots further. If you are like most people, you'll continue to store the cooked meat in your fridge for another however-many-days-you-can-get-away-with!

Raising animals for food has become a mega industry, so animals are unnecessarily treated to produce certain textures of meat or impregnated to produce an overabundance of milk. This kind of food product is totally different from the wild animal fare that your ancestors would catch on a hunt and, guess what, the health effect of farm-raised animal fare is entirely different too ... and not in a good way.

It becomes a no-brainer then that vegetarian foods are easier for your body to assimilate. Add to this the fact that they delay premature ageing. Foods such as meat, eggs, fish, sweets, cheese, potatoes and root vegetables that are high in protein and produce high levels of physical energy are referred to as *rajasic* foods. You can get away with this kind of diet until you reach middle age. After this however, like all things, your digestive system ages and finds it challenging to assimilate the kind of food you are fed when younger.

Rajasic foods become increasingly difficult to digest post-middle age and often accumulate as toxins.

The toxins that arise out of rajasic and tamasic foods are unctuous or oily in nature and are typically stored in the body's fat tissues. With excess eating, especially low quality rajasic and tamasic foods, your body's toxins will accumulate and your physical body often responds by generating more fat cells to house them. And you wondered why, despite all the exercise, you weren't able to shed the excess poundage you've accumulated over the years. It is for this simple reason that detoxification generally leads to weight loss.

Ayurvedic doctors recommend a diet that incorporates organic foods that are pure and close to nature – a *sattvic* diet with plenty of fresh fruits, vegetables, nuts, seeds that are combined with herbs and spices will purify and balance the mind and body. Sattvic foods that are freshly prepared tend to be more alkaline and metabolize efficiently. They are considered high-quality foods that maximize ojas or life-sap and lead to purity of the mind. This, by the way, is not a loosey-goosey concept to be scoffed at. All too often, our daily emotions are filled with negativity; you could be filled with road rage trying to drive to work or you may envy your colleague or even be judgemental about your neighbours when you return home. Well, I'm sorry to tell you folks, but those negative feelings do absolutely nothing for enhancing digestion and absolutely everything for releasing toxins into your system. It's a vicious cycle in the mind-body process.

2. Ayurveda is not a vegetarian philosophy

Contrary to popular belief, Ayurveda is not a vegetarian philosophy. In fact, its ancient texts provide detailed ways and means of preparing meats. Most Ayurvedic doctors and clinicians however, tend to adopt a largely vegetarian take on Ayurvedic cuisine as it is considered to be 'karmically inappropriate' to kill animals. From a general health point of view, animal foods are becoming increasingly toxic as we continue to industrialize food production. Gone are the days of hunting and wild farming, so you have to be really careful about where and how you buy your meats. Also, vegetarian foods detoxify and purify the mind-body as much as they build it.

Although not every Ayurvedic doctor will advise against eating fish, meat and eggs. In general, it can be said that the Ayurvedic diet is best served by lacto-vegetarianism. In cultures that exemplify man-made environments and fast-paced lifestyles, vegetarian foods are easier for the body to assimilate and also delay premature ageing. Furthermore, organically grown vegetarian foods detoxify and purify the mind-body as much as they build it.

Given these reasons and given green living trends that focus on vegetarianism, I have provided exclusively vegetarian recipes. My recipes include a variety of plant-based ingredients, they favour whole grains rather than processed grains and sugars and select healing ingredients that help maintain a healthy weight. That said, I have also included various hints about which non-vegetarian produce is ideal for your body type depending on the season at hand. The list of resources at the end of the book will include (as best as possible) places where free-range non-vegetarian produce is available.

3. Eating Ayurvedically doesn't mean eating desi food only

Despite the general consensus, Ayurvedic cooking does not have to exclusively yield 'Indian food'. As long as it is prepared as per Ayurvedic principles, it can fit into just about any cuisine. Traditionally, Ayurvedic doctors and health centres have served dal, chawal and khichadi primarily because that is the staple of Indian cuisine. Ayurvedic specialists, if not doctors, are growing in numbers throughout the world and as individuals continue to explore different cuisines and cultural food preparations, the principles of Ayurveda have gone well beyond Indian borders.

Because I like eating a variety of cuisines, I have always encouraged my Ayurvedic clients to cook however they like as long as their meals adhere to Ayurvedic principles. The recipes in this book range from pure Indian foods to Indo-West 'fusion' cuisine, incorporating Ayurvedic herbs and ingredients that can be sourced fresh and locally. The emphasis here is on providing culinary instruction that provides flavourful cuisine. One which beautifully presented, simple to prepare, yet easy for the body to assimilate into the raw building blocks for health and vitality.

4. Ghee aids weight loss and lowers cholesterol

Common thinking tells us that ghee leads to weight-gain and builds cholesterol in your arteries. Not true and quite the opposite in fact! Ayurveda has been using ghee for thousands of years to do quite the opposite – to rid the body of toxins which clog up the channels and create problems for the heart and most other organ systems. The oily or unctuous nature of ghee has a similar characteristic to that of a toxin which is why it is one of the greatest solvents that will, like Pac-Man, attack fatty toxins lodged in your tissues to loosen, liquefy and extract them through the regular digestive process.

Not only that – ghee is vital to feed and build the dhaatus and pacify the vata and pitta doshas. Did you know that a hundred-year-old ghee was known to be an instant cure for nervous-system disorders? Back in the days of yore, Indian households would store ghee in large vats and pass it down from generation to generation. Today it is hard enough to persuade a family member to make the ghee at home, let alone store it.

Of course the medicinal aspects of ghee depends upon what kind of ghee you are using – most people in India have grown used to eating commercially-made products that are a long way from, and do not have the properties of traditional desi ghee. It is a well-known fact that the industrialization of ghee means that manufacturers churn it in heavy-duty food processors that actually induce heat into the product. This is quite different from traditional hand-churned ghee which is laborious to make, but maintains its original cooling energy which is integral to making it medicinal.

In Chapter 5, there are instructions on how to make your own ghee. Again it's a laborious process, but well worth the effort.

5. Eating ginger before your meal powers up digestion, enabling you to keep your weight in check

Eating Ayurvedically is all about improving the efficiency of your digestive system. Perfect digestion is the core of perfect health, and imperfect digestion leads to things like weight gain, toxic overload and illness. Therefore, the principles of Ayurvedic 'ahar', or food as medicine, among other things include pre- and post-digestive tips like eating ginger before a meal to stimulate your 'agni' or digestive fire. It's akin to powering up an engine to make it function better. If the engine is powered up then naturally it's functioning, i.e., the digestion will also be better. The Japanese who are pros with this concept have actually cultivated the habit from Ayurveda. We in India on the other hand have conveniently forgotten these things.

6. The right amount of water to maintain lubrication and weight balance is as many glasses as the hours you are awake in a day

We have grown too used to the standard Western dietary prescription of six to eight glasses of water a day. Much as we'd love to believe it, this is not the magic number just because the Western diet books say so. If only life were that simple! You have to think of yourself as a garden – if watered at night, you will naturally retain more moisture. Once the sun comes out however, the water begins to evaporate and all your plants and the soil get parched. On longer days (like in the summer), this happens to a greater extent. It's the same way with humans – the more time you spend awake during the day, the more water you need to keep yourself lubricated and healthy.

7. Do not undergo strict fasting for more than a day – it messes up your digestion and leads to weight gain

Fasting is a common concept in India and the common thinking is that fasting gives your digestive system a break and enhances weight loss. Not exactly. 'Fasting', according to Ayurveda, means 'limited' food and never complete abstinence. This can be achieved through one to three days of phal-sabzi-ahar regimes, etc., but never through pure starvation (for more than a twenty-four-hour stretch) for the simple reason that if you stay off food and drink completely, your system confuses the signals between your brain and your digestive system and ruins the efficiency of the digestive process.

Many religious fasts in India have an Ayurvedic origin but, if you notice, these are not pure abstinence regimes as much as they are protocols for restricting certain foods at certain times.

Now it is a good idea to undergo what is loosely termed as a fruit-and-veggie fast a couple of times a year. But again, these are not fasts as much as they are detox exercises designed to give your digestion a break and reboot the overall health of your immune system. You can do three to four such detoxes at different times during the year. Or longer, five to seven day detoxes a couple of times a year – ideally during the fall and the spring seasons.

8. Eat according to the seasons

Ayurveda recommends that you select foods and adjust your eating patterns according to the seasons. The change in seasons affects your mind-body. If you don't shift your nutritional and lifestyle patterns to balance what is happening in the environment, your health can be off-kilter. This doesn't mean you have to completely reinvent your life every few months, but instead, we should make small changes to live in harmony with the seasons.

While the supermarket can provide all foods all year round, there is wisdom in eating warming foods in winter and cooling fruits during the summer. Try eating fresh and organically grown produce, fruits and vegetables that are available through farms and suppliers close to where you live to be sure that you are in tune with the season and surrounding geography. This makes the perfect reason to sign up for community-supported agriculture or to start visiting your local farmers market regularly.

9. At any meal never eat more in one meal than what you can hold in one anjali

Your two palms cupped together comprises what is known in Ayurveda as one anjali, and that is just about the amount of food your stomach can digest at any one given meal. Now you may look at your two hands and think, 'Well, that's not a lot of food.' Guess what, you are absolutely right. Your stomach is not huge – it can contain just one anjali-ful of food, gastric juices and vata to actually churn all of this together. Anything more means you are overloading it and hindering the digestive process. When this happens, food remains undigested and begins to accumulate toxins. Eating one anjali-ful of food will keep you satiated. Remember, when this is digested, no one is stopping you from eating again.

10. Lunch should be the main meal of the day

Noon is when the sun is positioned directly overhead. I don't think I need to tell you that – it's a fundamental fact which you have known since you were a child. But what you probably didn't know is that when the sun shines overhead, your powers of digestion, your main agni is at its strongest. Because agni is related to pitta, this is one reason why the pitta dosha types feel hungry (to the point of being crabby) at lunch time. But regardless of which dosha dominates your prakruti, this is the time of the day when you are able to most efficiently digest whatever you eat. Even though we have evolved our social lives to have large, and often late, dinners, this schedule actually interferes with your basic health and disrupts your sleep pattern. As you grow older this grows more and more apparent.

Ayurvedically speaking, lunch should be your main meal of the day and as you age, if you find yourself adjusting to fewer meals in a day, this is the one that is definitely not to be missed. If you can work towards a new normal by using the meal suggestions in this book for lunch, along with a light breakfast, a light dinner and perhaps a few in-between snacks if necessary, you'll be doing your digestive system a huge favour. Eating heavy meals several times a day only causes the system to overload and gives you the fake belief that gluttony is normal.

11. Eat before the turn of the day

Ayurveda tells you that daytime is the time of absorption and night-time is the time of accumulation. This means that your body is designed to digest food during daylight. Eating after dark is not a good idea as the food will tend to sit there accumulating rather than digest.

As such, it is a good idea to eat your last meal early – by, or preferably before, sunset. Bear in mind of course that things change during the different seasons of the year. Therefore, in summer, when the days are longer, you have more leeway for eating dinner later in the evening. However, come winter, you'll want to finish your meals earlier. As soon as darkness descends, that is the time to hibernate – in winter, everyone needs more rest and longer sleeping hours.

12. Eating Ayurvedically is not about eating in one particular way

Most popular diets require you to restrict your eating patterns to particular types of food. So raw diets ask you to cut out cooked food, low- or no-carb diets restrict starches and grains in favour of high-protein and high-fat foods, and the lists go on.

The Ayurvedic diet is quite different. Essentially, the requirement here works like this:

1. Working on the assumption that you are healthy, you eat according to the seasons, looking to tweak your diet if necessary to balance your dosha type. Following the recipes and eating guidelines in this book are ideal.

2. Working on the assumption that you are not on top of your game, but not considerably unhealthy, you eat to balance your dosha. Balancing your dosha takes priority over eating according to the season (although the two an inextricably interlinked). You can still however, follow many of the recipes from this book as long as you tweak them to fix the unbalanced dosha.

3. Working on the assumption that you are suffering from an illness, you check in with an Ayurvedic doctor and follow his/her guidelines for a strict dietary regime (outside the scope of this book) until you are healthy enough to pick up the reins once again and follow the above plans.

This means that there is no 'standard diet' that you follow every single day of your life. Life is dynamic, so are the seasons. So too are your eating patterns. Too many of us just mix up a salad here and a dal there. Raw foods are ideal for certain times of the year – the seasons dominated by the kapha or pitta dosha for example – but not necessarily during other seasons and certainly never for dinner, the last meal of the day. As long as you know when to eat raw versus when to eat cooked foods, you will not get gain weight.

Also, while many recipes call for the use of whole grains or whole-grain derivatives, it is always ideal to sprout them first for maximum nutritional benefit. The sprouting process changes the nutrient composition of the grains to activate enzymes, increase protein quality and maximize absorption of soluble vitamins and fibres. Again, this requires more time and effort so we tend to not do this – for example, to make roti, we use wheat flour which is essentially ground wheat. What we should be using is sprouted wheat berry that is then ground into a mix and used for making rotis. This is more or less applicable for any grain, and while it might change the texture of the roti from what you are accustomed to eating right now, it will do wonders for your health and weight.

13. If you combine foods correctly according to Ayurveda, you will not fall sick or put on weight

There are many food combinations that your parents or grandparents have traditionally advised you against: not to have hot and cold foods simultaneously, or no milk and fruit at the same time. Yet, I'll bet my last rupee that you don't flinch about having things like mango lassi for example, a classic modern milk-and-fruit combination.

Regardless of what you have become used to eating, there are a handful of basic no-no's when it comes to eating for optimum health. There are multiple rules, but all of them are hard to describe in great detail. Some foods do not combine well with others, sometimes because they have opposing qualities or gunas or vipak/virya. Other combinations are bad because the foods become incompatible in the cooking process. At other times, things don't work well because the foods eaten at certain times during the day exacerbate the dosha energies prevalent at those times of the day.

Getting into every rule is not easy, but here is a basic list of absolute no-no's that everyone should be aware:

○ No dairy with fruit, radish or raisins – essentially fruits digest very quickly, whereas milk takes longer to process. During this time, the fruit can curdle the milk creating acidity. Radish is heating, whereas dairy is cooling. Dairy is a complete food – it should not be combined with anything else as it takes a long time to digest

○ No milk with meat or fish – fish and meat are heating, whereas dairy is cooling. As such combining the two creates blockages and toxins

○ No salt and milk – salt is astringent, whereas milk nourishes the tissues

○ Ice cream, iced or cold drinks during or right after a meal – these hamper agni or digestive fire

○ No yoghurt or sweet foods after 6 p.m. kapha energies are high during this time of the day which means that eating kaphic foods will enhance excess mucous production

○ No cooked honey – raw honey is medicinal, but cooked honey changes its chemical nature to a sticky, gluey toxic substance that clogs your srotas or channels

○ Do not combine ghee and honey – ghee is cooling and honey is heating. As a result they are incompatible during the digestive process

○ No fruits with potatoes, or other starchy foods, fried foods and cheese – for the same reason you would not mix milk with fruit. Fruits digest very quickly while other foods take a longer time. Fruit is best had alone – the one exception is that sour fruits such as strawberries, tomatoes, currants, grapefruit, lemon, orange, pineapple can be combined with proteins (but not milk) since they have an alkalizing net energetic effect

o Sour fruits should not be combined with sweet fruits such as bananas, dates, dried fruits and figs

o Melons and grains – melons digest quickly whereas grains take more time. This combination will upset the stomach. Melons should be eaten alone

o Nightshades like potato, tomato or eggplant should not be combined with yogurt, milk, melon, cucumber

o Starches should not be combined with eggs, milk, bananas or dates

o Lighter foods such as corn should not be combined with heavier foods like dates, raisins, banana

o Eggs should not be combined with milk, meat, yogurt, melons, cheese, fish, banana – the body has a difficult time digesting large amounts of protein. It is far better to choose one type of protein and pair it with vegetables

o No milk with bananas, sour fruits – lemons, oranges, plums, melons, curds, cherries – this combination slows digestion and generates toxins

o No fruits with potato, tapioca, other starches due to different rates of digestion

o No stale, frozen, canned, fried foods or left-overs, food additives – as mentioned earlier, these are considered to be tamasic

○ No sweet or heavy flour-based desserts after a meal. Eating these before a meal is alright as kapha digestion happens first

○ No refined food especially grains and sugar made into flour and pastes – like pasta, bread, etc.

○ Do not eat within three hours of bedtime. Undigested food in the stomach interferes with sleep patterns. Furthermore, sleep does not support digestion

HOW TO GO ABOUT YOUR EVERYDAY EATING

You may be familiar with the old adage 'what you are is what you eat', but I am willing to wager that nobody has told you how you eat it is just as important. If you truly want to achieve perfect digestion then it's important to understand that the quality of your digestion is directly related to what goes on in your mind-body and in your environment.

Let me put this in context. Ever wonder why happy social gatherings at the dining table are so conducive to perfect digestion, or when you were a child, did your parents ever tell you not to eat and read at the same time? Here's how this works – the autonomic nervous system takes charge of digestion automatically, but since it has two aspects, sympathetic and parasympathetic, which operate in a contrary manner, the results of digestion can either be good or bad. When your mind-body is at rest, then your parasympathetic nervous system dominates. Digestion and elimination proceed normally.

On the other hand, if your mind is focused on reading

while you are eating, or frankly on other things like work or politics, then the energy of digestion is basically diverted away from the activity of digestion. If you are particularly emotionally charged while you are eating, then your sympathetic nervous system functioning dominates – your blood supply is shunted to the peripheral muscles away from the stomach, etc., digestive juices stop flowing and the peristalsis of elimination stops.

What does that lead to? Undigested food matter and toxins. Here are a few things to bear in mind to optimize digestion:

- Eat in a calm atmosphere to support the functioning of the parasympathetic nervous system
- Eat mindfully for emotional satisfaction. Enjoy the tastes, the appearance, the smell and the textures of the food. All too often we rush through our meals without savouring the flavours of the food, but once you try this you'll understand how this completely alters your meal and you'll wonder why you never did this before
- Don't read or watch television while eating – focus only on the meal
- Social meals are fine, but don't talk unnecessarily while eating and certainly not when you have food in your mouth
- Listen to soft, gentle, healing music during your meal
- Eat without attachment or aversion
- Brush your teeth after each meal to prevent bacterial build-up in the mouth
- Improve your digestion by lying on your left side for about ten minutes after eating

○ Take a short walk after your meal. This supports digestion

○ Avoid strenuous exercise within two hours of eating

○ Eat only the amount of food which fits into your two hands, or one anjali, approximately $1/3$ in solid foods, $1/3$ liquids and $1/3$ for vata to churn the food in your stomach

○ Chew your food well – about thirty-two times for each bite before you swallow. Salivary amylase, a digestive secretion in the saliva, begins digesting carbohydrates while in the mouth. The problem with many of us is that we end up swallowing too quickly, so mouth digestion is left incomplete

○ Consider a liquid fast of fresh fruit and vegetable juice, one day each week. Ideally, the same day of the week consistently would be best. This gives the digestive and eliminative systems an opportunity to rest and clean

○ Use glass for cooking or baking whenever possible. For stove-top cooking, use pots and pans made of cast iron, stainless steel, and copper. Avoid non-stick surfaced cooking utensils.

Planning for the family table

One question that I am asked a lot is how to plan for the family table. Does each person need to have a special meal cooked for them? The answer is no. Here is the general rule:

1. Prepare your family meal to balance the dosha of the season.

2. Have some condiments ready at hand to allow your individual family member to tweak seasonings and dressing to meet the individual needs of their dosha. For example, oil, herbs, spices, nuts and seeds are all condiments that can be added as food

toppings to help meet dosha-balancing needs. Choose from the ingredient lists provided earlier in this chapter or some of the set dosha recipes in the next chapter.

3. End your meals with herbal dosha-balancing teas and digestive munchies like saunf to support everyone's particular digestive needs.

4. Lunch should be the main meal, dinner before the end of the day.

PART II

Recipes

5

Stocking Your Ayurvedic Kitchen

The recipes detailed in the next chapter call for a number of ingredients, some common, some perhaps less familiar and some that might be completely new to you. This chart lists the staples of any Ayurvedic pantry and explains their significant properties for Ayurvedic practices. As you learn more about your dosha and the imbalances you tend to experience, you will find yourself customizing this list to meet your personal needs regardless of the season.

Ayurvedic herbal ingredients are available in Ayurvedic shops, natural-food stores and mail-order suppliers (see Resources, page 180). Shop in places where you know the stock is turned over frequently and try to use fresh herbs whenever possible. If you just cannot find fresh herbs, then opt for whole dried herbs. Bear in mind though that dried herbs begin to lose effectiveness after about two to three months, even sooner when ground, so buy only a little at a time. Or better still, buy them whole and grind them at home as and when required, using a mortar and pestle.

Some of these ingredients can be found in compounds

such as dosha-balancing teas or triphala, so look out for them as you shop.

YOUR AYURVEDIC PANTRY

Oils and Ghee

Coconut (nariyal) oil: This cooling oil is extremely stable and is ideal for balancing pitta. Use it interchangeably with ghee in the seasons when pitta is aggravated.

Ghee: Known in culinary terms as clarified butter, this is a tissue-builder, detoxifier and ideal for balancing vata (as it is extremely penetrating) and pitta (as it is sweet and cooling). You will find ghee used in many recipes. It is important to use ghee that has been prepared in the traditional style and not a big brand that has been processed like commercial butter as they can actually be harmful for your health. See also page 96 for instructions on making your own ghee.

Mustard (sarson) oil: This healing oil is ideal for balancing kapha. A common ingredient in late winter and spring cooking.

Sesame (til) oil: This warming, nutritious oil is suitable for all three doshas, particularly for vata.

Medicinal Herbs

Amla: This fruit has a high content of vitamin C and is full of antioxidants. It increases ojas in all tissues and is powerful for balancing pitta in the blood cells and tissues.

Brahmi: Translated as 'divine creative energy', this rejuvenating herb, known to calm and cool the mind, is ideal for balancing pitta and vata. A *rasayan* herb, it is believed to promote intelligence and eternal youth, and can be used in teas and salads.

Dashmool: Meaning 'ten valuables or roots', it is a mixture containing the roots of ten key medicinal herbs. Ideal as a herb tea, this is a powerful ally in the flu season.

Neem: This bitter herb is celebrated for its antiseptic, blood-detoxifying and skin-healing properties. Fresh neem, it's juice or even dried neem powder all work wonders in helping round off dishes with a classic bitter taste.

Triphala: The three fruits – amalaki, bibhitaki and haritaki – comprised in this mix balance each of the three doshas and cleanse the entire digestive system. Key to seasonal detoxifying programmes, triphala may be consumed everyday – as a tea with milk, or mixed with honey or ghee. This great overall digestive blend of three different herbs consists of – amalaki which pacifies pitta, haritaki which pacifies kapha and bibhitaki which pacifies vata.

Tulsi: This plant, known as the holy basil, has properties that aid in building immunity and preventing illnesses. Look for fresh tulsi leaves or better still purchase a plant for your home.

Haldi (turmeric): A powerful blood-purifier, this is a common cooking spice. Most people use dried haldi, but as far as possible, try to use fresh haldi.

Kala namak: No Indian kitchen is without kala namak which is actually pink rather than black (as suggested by its name) in colour, but most people are not aware of its powerful role as a digestive aid. Kala namak, a cooling spice in Ayurvedic medicine, is used as a laxative and a general digestive aid to relieve intestinal gas and heartburn. It is also wonderful for stabilizing blood pressure.

Other Foods and Plants

Kumari (aloe): A cooling plant that grows in hot desert terrains, this pitta-balancing gel is ideal both as a salad dressing ingredient and as a juice mix.

Ginger: An important Ayurvedic ingredient, this vata- and kapha-balancing root is useful for teas, salads and food flavouring.

Malai (cream): Highly nutritious and moisturizing, this is the perfect vata-balancing food

Madhu (honey): A natural sweetener, ideal for tempering the challenging tastes of some Ayurvedic medicinal herbs. Keep in mind, only raw honey is medicinal. Cooked honey is extremely toxic.

Gulab jal (rose water): An ideal coolant that is added to a variety of dishes.

Yoghurt: The perfect digestive aid, yoghurt is a must for any Ayurvedic kitchen. Make sure you make it every day and consume as soon as possible to maximize the pro-biotic effect.

You do not of course, need to be limited by this Ayurvedic pantry. The more you become accustomed to cooking Ayurvedically, you buy, store and experiment with a variety of medicinal plants. Page 180 in the Resources section of this book provides a long list of medicinal herbs that you can use in your cooking.

BASIC RECIPES

There are a few common foods which have been referred to over and over again in the recipes that follow. Although many of these can be purchased in a store, there is nothing quite like making them at home from scratch. It's not rocket science and frankly, it gives you more control over what you are putting into your stomach. Listed here are a few generic recipes for basic foods that you can prepare in advance and use for your cooking.

Basic Vegetable Stock

I use vegetable stock extensively in my Ayurvedic cooking. It can be used in any recipe that requires water. So cooking rice or millet or barley for example, in vegetable stock gives you a much more flavourful outcome than simply cooking in water.

Nowadays you can buy vegetable stock in the store, but really, that is so unnecessary. It's one of the easiest things to make at home and doesn't require too much time either. It just requires a handful of basic vegetables, pretty much any vegetables that are in season. You can keep a large tupperware container in the fridge and throw in things like veggies that have wilted beyond saving, the stalks or green parts from root vegetables, carrot trimmings, and so on. As soon as the tupperware gets full, you can use the contents to make a broth. You can also tailor it to your own needs, adding garlic or other spices if you like. I prefer to make mine fairly basic without adding salt or too many spices because those are things I can actually add while making the recipe itself.

INGREDIENTS
1 to 2 onions
2 to 3 carrots
3 to 4 celery stalks
4 to 5 sprigs fresh thyme (or any other herb like coriander, tulsi, etc.)
1 bay leaf
1 small bunch of parsley
1 teaspoon of whole peppercorns
Optional extras: green onions (whole, including the green part), fennel, tomatoes, mushrooms, mushroom stems, turnips

METHOD

- *Stockpile your vegetables and herbs. Onions, carrots and celery make a great base, but you can mix and match and choose any of the other vegetables listed above. If, for some reason, you cannot find a particular veggie listed above then you can also make stock using any amount of vegetables that you happen to have at hand. Aim for roughly equal portions of each so the stock has a balanced flavour.*

- *Wash any visible dirt off the vegetables and then chop them coarsely. You don't even need to peel them first unless you really want to. That includes onions.*

- *In a large pot, place all the vegetables and cover with enough water so that you can easily stir the contents of the pot. Less water means your stock will be more concentrated; more water makes a lighter-flavoured stock.*

- *Set the pot on medium-high heat and bring it to just under a boil. Once you start to see some bubbling around the edges of the pot and a few wisps of steam on the surface, turn the heat down to medium-low.*

- *Cook for approximately an hour. Again, go by the principle of andaaze se. There is no exact science, but generally one hour is enough time to infuse the water with the nutrients from the veggies. Stir the pot every once in a while to circulate the vegetables.*
- *Take the pot off the stove and remove all the vegetables with a slotted ladle. Strain the vegetable stock through a cheesecloth.*
- *Divide the stock into storage containers, cool completely. Store in the fridge (for up to a week) before using.*

GHEE – THE LONGEVITY ENHANCER

In Ayurveda ghee, or clarified butter, is believed to be one of the most sattvic foods, as it promotes memory, intelligence, agni and ojas. Excellent for all three doshas, though specifically for vata and pitta, ghee is ideal for cooking as it has a high smoke point and does not burn easily. It provides nourishment to the body and builds healthy tissues when used in cooking, when taken alone or when prepared with medicinal herbs.

Although ghee is readily available at Indian grocery stores, it is fairly simple to make your own at home. I do not suggest making it from milk cream as it requires extensive churning to turn it into butter. Although you can churn the cream with a mixer, I am not in favour of machine-churned butter as this upsets the natural cooling property of ghee. You can, of course, make ghee from hand-churned organic butter. Here's how:

- *Clean and sterilize a saucepan by filling it with water, cover it with the lid and bring it to boil for thirty minutes.*
- *Discard the water and add one pound of unsalted organic hand-churned butter cut into chunks into the pan and heat over low*

heat for ten to fifteen minutes until the foam that collects on the surface begins to settle at the bottom of the pan.

- *Continue to cook, stirring the top occasionally, until the ghee begins to boil gently.*
- *Remove from the heat source and let it cool.*
- *Pour the clarified butter on top into a clean container, leaving the sediment at the bottom of the pan. As long as it is kept away from moisture and other contaminants, ghee keeps indefinitely without refrigeration because the milk fats that cause butter to spoil have been removed.*

At room temperature, ghee can be solid or semi-solid, depending upon the climate. Cooler weather will solidify the ghee, so run warm water over the closed container to soften it if necessary. But, unlike butter, you do not need to keep this in the fridge.

Coconut Milk

INGREDIENTS
½ cup of fresh grated coconut
½ cup of water

METHOD
- *Grind the coconut with water and squeeze out the thick milk with a strainer.*
- *Put the extracted coconut back into the grinder.*
- *Add some water and then squeeze out the thin milk.*
- *Strain again and squeeze the coconut completely.*

Homemade White Butter

INGREDIENTS
2 or 3 cups of fresh cream (malai)
½ to 1 cup of water

METHOD

- *You can buy ready-made full cream from the grocery store. Alternatively, you can collect cream from the milk you use daily, but if you do this, make sure you store it in a freezer.*
- *Defrost the cream.*
- *In a food-processor add the cream to ½ to one cup of water.*
- *Cream will begin to smoothen into whipped cream.*
- *Continue mixing until the butter separates from buttermilk.*
- *Strain the butter from the buttermilk through a fine strainer.*

DOSHA CHURNAS

Dosha churnas are essentially blends of Ayurvedic herbs that you can store in your pantry and use in a variety of dishes. You can brew them and drink them as teas or stronger decoctions for soup bases. You can also use them in tadkas, salad dressing or just toss them into your herb mix when you prepare any dish. I find them to be a particularly convenient way to tweak dishes for dosha-balancing needs.

Although the following recipe suggests combining three tablespoonsful of each ingredient, you can make as much or as little of each churna as you like. Remember, when it comes to Ayurvedic cooking it's all about andaaze se. You can also tweak the churna recipes to include more or less of any particular herb to alter the overall taste of the blend or the medicinal impact.

Experiment with both fresh as well as dried churnas. As far as possible, I always prefer blends using fresh herbs. If it means that you need to cut down on some of the ingredients for each churna, that's fine. The following recipes assume you are using dried, whole herbs. If you need to grind them into a powder, it is better to prepare a whole herb mix and then grind into a powder as and when you need it. If you need to alter the recipes below to just use dried powders, then that's fine too, but you should try and finish this as soon as possible, so perhaps adjust down to one or two tablespoonsful of each ingredient. If however, you can use fresh herbs and spices, so much the better. Just cut down the ingredients to ½ teaspoonful to one teaspoonful of each and put them together on the day of your cooking with the aim of using them up the same day.

And finally, try your very best to use organic sources. This means becoming picky and choosy about who you buy from, generally a good habit if you want to be healthy! A list of suppliers can be found on page 180.

Pitta Churna

INGREDIENTS
3 tablespoonsful of coriander seeds
3 tablespoonsful of fennel seeds
3 tablespoonsful of cumin seeds
3 tablespoonsful of jaggery or date sugar
3 tablespoonsful of cardamom pods
3 tablespoonsful of ginger, chopped
3 tablespoonsful of turmeric, chopped
3 tablespoonsful of rock salt (kala namak), whole
3 tablespoonsful of liquorice
3 tablespoonsful of amla
3 tablespoonsful of neem leaves

METHOD
- *Add all ingredients to an air-tight jar.*
- *Close the lid and shake vigorously until the spices are well mixed.*

sary to brew into teas, soup bases, in salad dressing,
t sprinkle over food for added flavour.

INGREDIENTS

3 tablespoonsful of cumin seeds
3 tablespoonsful of ginger, chopped
3 tablespoonsful of turmeric, dried and chopped
3 tablespoonsful of jaggery or date sugar
3 tablespoonsful of ajwain
3 tablespoonsful of salt, whole
3 tablespoonsful of asafoetida, whole
3 tablespoonsful of ashwagandha
3 tablespoonsful of kantakari

METHOD

- *Add all ingredients to an air-tight jar.*
- *Close the lid and shake vigorously until the spices are well mixed.*
- *Use as necessary to brew into teas, soups bases, in salad dressing, tadkas or just sprinkle over food for added flavour.*

Kapha Churna

INGREDIENTS

3 tablespoonsful of ginger, chopped
3 tablespoonsful of black pepper
3 tablespoonsful of haritaki
3 tablespoonsful of turmeric, chopped and dried
3 tablespoonsful of rock salt (kala namak), whole
3 tablespoonsful of cinnamon sticks
3 tablespoonsful of fenugreek seeds
3 tablespoonsful of neem, chopped, fresh

METHOD

- *Add all ingredients to an air-tight jar.*
- *Close the lid and shake vigorously until the spices are well mixed.*

✓ Use as necessary to brew into teas, soup bases, in salad dressing, tadkas or just sprinkle over food for added flavour.

SWARAS KALPANA – JUICE OF THE HERBS

Translated from Sanskrit, *Swaras Kalpana* refers to a procedure rather than an actual recipe. It is a procedure described in ancient Ayurvedic texts to extract fresh juice from herbs. As a matter of fact, there are several such procedures described and, at the risk of sounding complicated, they are all actually quite simple and can be applied to just about any Ayurvedic medicinal herb. Here are a few different methods for you to experiment with:

Fresh Herb Juice Extraction
✓ Collect fresh herbs and clean them thoroughly to remove dirt
✓ Cut into small pieces and pound them with a mortar and pestle to get a soft paste.
✓ Squeeze the juice from the herbal paste using a clean cotton cloth.
✓ Collect this juice in a vessel.
✓ Repeat the process until the pounded herbal paste loses its original taste (rendering all flavour to the juice instead)

Dry Herb Juice Extraction
✓ If fresh herbs are not available, then dried herbs can be used to extract juice.
✓ Soak one part of the dried herb with two parts of water. Leave it overnight.
✓ Pound the soaked herb and extract the juice.
✓ Follow the same steps of fresh herb juice extraction

Powdered Dry Herb Juice Extraction

- *Add one part of dried powdered herb to eight parts of water.*
- *Boil this until ¼th of water remains.*
- *Filter the herb and use the liquid part to drink or for your recipe*

JUICE EXTRACTION FROM HARD HERBS

When you use hard fresh herbs like barks or hard stems, juice extraction can be challenging. Another method explained in Ayurvedic pharmacology is as follows:

- *Wrap the hard herb pieces in a cloth and place in a steel box.*
- *Cook these herbs in a pressure cooker to soften them.*
- *Allow the herbs to cool.*
- *Pound this and extract the juice as described earlier*

A few things to note:

- *Freshly prepared juice must be used immediately. Storing in the refrigerator is absolutely out of the question.*
- *If you like, you can add other ingredients like honey, jaggery, pepper, cumin seed powder, ghee, salt, etc., to enhance the taste and medicinal properties of the herbal juice.*
- *If you plan to drink the juice rather than use in cooking, then figure about 25 ml of fresh herbal juice or 50 ml of dried herbal juice.*

Copper water

Again, this one is more of a simple procedure than a recipe. The healing properties of water infused with weak ions of copper, are immense. Copper helps strengthen the immune system and helps prevent anaemia. Infusing water with copper is simple enough:

- Fill a clean copper vessel with water and boil on low heat until the water quantity is halved. Better still, you can store water in a clean copper vessel and drink after eight to twelve hours. Storing for a longer period is also fine, but prepare yourself for a slightly metallic taste. This is because of a larger concentration of copper ions. An ideal morning habit involves drinking water that has been stored in a copper vessel overnight.
- Remember to keep the inside of your copper vessel clean and shiny. Opt for something natural to clean it, like tamarind. This is so much better than chemical cleaners.

6

Sharad Ritu

MEALS TO PACIFY PITTA ELEMENTS IN THE ENVIRONMENT

Sharad Ritu or the autumn season lasts from mid-September to about mid-November. During this season, the sudden exposure to sunlight after the rains aggravates the pitta dosha. It is best then to have a diet of easily digestible food with sweet, bitter, cold energies to combat pitta. Above all, avoid heavy foods, curds, oils and alcohol.

Agni or digestive fire follows the patterns of the sun. That means two things:

○ Your digestive power is strongest when the sun is directly overhead – more or less at noon (between 10 a.m. and 2 p.m.). At daybreak, agni is mild, just like the strength of the sun at dawn. By noon, it gathers strength and is the strongest; just like the heat at noon. The agni gradually diminishes in strength as an evening sun would. Agni wanes as dusk approaches and is weakest at dinner time.

○ Your digestive power is strongest during Sharad Ritu. During this season, the days are longer so you spend more waking hours eating, exercising and generally going about your day. While you might be able to get away with raw foods, heavier meals and sweeter foods during this season, they should be tempered with cooling ingredients that counter the overall pitta doshas in the environment. Of course, each meal can be further tweaked to meet your individual dosha type.

Breakfasts during the pitta aggravating season should be light enough to digest and also be nourishing enough to sustain you through the first portion of the day. This is the season to have an entirely raw breakfast or a combination of raw and cooked breakfast. Lunch can be large and primarily raw. Dinner should be lighter than the other meals.

Suggested meal combinations for Sharad Ritu:
- Cold pea soup with rosewater
- Okra, pomegranate and coconut salad
- Barley khichadi with sunflower sprouts
- Saffron lassi, coconut flatbread and lima beans with thyme and anantamul, arugula, and mung dal salad
- Sautéed bean sprouts with coriander chutney, plain rice and cucumber soup
- Cabbage rolls with watercress, dates and mushrooms with a sesame-cilantro aioli, mint lassi
- Kokum soup, barley or millet with pitta churna tadka, raw papaya and turmeric salad
- Pitta snack time: seasonal tea or kokum cooler and coconut-tulsi cookies

RECIPES

Cold Pea Soup with Rosewater
(Serves Six)

Rosewater is a wonderful antidote to pitta energies and green peas are more digestible during the pitta season, which makes them a great summer food. Even so, adding herbs and spices is always helpful.

INGREDIENTS

5 cups of fresh shelled peas (mattar)
3 cups of vegetable stock
1 cup of rosewater (gulab jal)
1 cup of sweet onion, chopped
½ cup of pea shoots (for garnish)
½ cup of fresh mint, chopped (pudina)
½ cup of fresh parsley, chopped
¼ cup of fresh garlic chives, chopped (for garnish)
2 tablespoons of coconut oil
2 teaspoons of sea salt
½ teaspoon of ground black pepper

METHOD

- In a large saucepan add the coconut oil and onion, cook over medium-low heat for five to ten minutes, until softened.
- Add the vegetable stock and increase the heat until mixture boils.
- Add the peas and cook for about five minutes until the peas are tender.
- Taking the pot off of the heat, add in fresh herbs, salt, pepper and adjust for seasonings (andaaze se).
- Puree the mixture in a blender a little at a time until the entire mixture is smooth and creamy.
- Add the rosewater and blend well into the mixture.
- Garnish with fresh cut chives, pumpkin seeds and pea shoots.

Tweak for Your Dosha:

Vata – instead of parsley, use tulsi

Pitta – replace the garlic chives with freshly chopped dill
Kapha – add chopped fresh ginger and/or kapha churna into the
seasoning

Barley Khichadi with Sunflower Sprouts
(Serves Two)

Here is a perfect khichadi for the hot summer months. It is
ideal to mix raw sunflower sprouts. If sunflower sprouts are
not available, then you can replace them with raw sprouts of
just about anything else – pumpkin, mung, dhaniya, etc., or
even raw leafy greens like spinach, fennel or cabbage.

INGREDIENTS
1 cup of barley (jau)
½ cup of split green gram
1 onion
½ cup of mixed vegetable – raw sunflower sprouts
4 cups of water or more – vegetable stock

SEASONING:
½ teaspoonful of cumin seeds
2 tablespoonsful of fresh amla juice or ½ teaspoonful of dried
amla
2 teaspoonsful of ghee
1 green chilli
2 cloves
2 to 3 cardamom pods
Salt as desired
A pinch of pippali

METHOD
- *Wash and soak the barley and green gram in clean water while you assemble the remaining ingredients for this recipe.*
- *Peel and chop onions and all the veggies you are using in the recipe.*
- *Slit the green chilli into two.*
- *Heat oil in a saucepan and add cumin seeds, cloves, amla,*

cardamom, pippali, green chilli and sliced onion. Sauté for a few minutes and add soaked barley and green gram.

⁍ *Pour two cups of water and cook until it becomes soft and mushy. Remove from the flame and lightly mash the cooked contents with the back of a ladle.*

⁍ *Pour two cups of hot water into the mushy khichadi and mix everything well. Add the sunflower sprouts and vegetables. Mix well.*

Tweak for Your Dosha:

Vata – if digestive energy is low, instead of barley use wheat, shastika (a fast-growing rice), or shali (a type of red rice); if you are healthy, then there is no need to change the recipe

Pitta – replace the garlic chives with freshly chopped dill

Kapha – add chopped fresh ginger and/or kapha churna into the seasoning; you can also replace barley with millet or rye

Okra, Pomegranate and Coconut Salad

(Serves Two)

INGREDIENTS

Salt

1 cup of okra (bhindi)

½ cup of pomegranate

2 tablespoonsful of ghee

½ teaspoonful of fennel seeds (saunf)

5 to 10 leaves of Indian borage (pathorchur)

½ cup of fresh, chopped coconut meat

SEASONING

Salt

A pinch of black pepper (andaaze se)

A pinch of liquorice (jeshtimadhu – also andaaze se)

½ cup of fresh orange juice

METHOD

⁍ *Boil a large pot of salted water.*

⁍ *Wash okra and cut off the stems. Slit the pods into half lengthwise*

- Seed the pomegranate.
- Heat ghee in a pan, add fennel seeds and sauté briefly. Add okra, and simmer for about five minutes.
- Mix together the orange juice, salt and pepper.
- Remove okra from heat. Add pomegranate and coconut meat.
- Pour seasoning over the salad.

Tweak for Your Dosha
Vata – add radish

Arugula and Mung Sprouts Salad
(Serves Six)

Arugula, more popularly known as rocket leaves, is a nutritious leafy green vegetable with a spicy and bitter bite. Available through the year, they make a perfect addition to any meal, but are ideal to eat during the warm summer days, right through the autumn season.

INGREDIENTS
2 cups of coarsely chopped arugula leaves (tara mira)
1 cup of mung sprouts

DRESSING
Juice of ½ a lemon
Garlic
Extra virgin olive oil
Salt
Pepper

METHOD
- Toss the salad together and season with the dressing.

Tweak for Your Dosha:
Vata – add sesame oil to the dressing

Sautéed Bean Sprouts and Turmeric
(Serves Six)

The great thing about beans is that you can sprout them to release their full enzyme potential. You can sprout just about any bean or lentil – mung, channa, rongi … be as creative as you like.

INGREDIENTS
½ cup of fresh turmeric (haldi), chopped
2 cups of bean sprouts
2 tablespoonsful of ghee
1 teaspoonful of coarsely ground coriander seeds
1 teaspoonful of mustard seeds
5 to 7 curry leaves
Salt
Pepper
Juice of ½ a lemon

METHOD
- *Warm the ghee, add coriander seeds, mustard seeds and curry leaves. Stir-fry for a few minutes until seeds pop.*
- *Add the turmeric and sauté for another few minutes.*
- *Add the bean sprouts and continue to sauté until the beans soften slightly but don't wait too long otherwise they tend to wilt.*
- *Add salt to taste, remove from fire.*
- *Squeeze lemon juice onto the stir-fry before serving.*

Tweak for Your Dosha:
Vata – add ½ teaspoonful of freshly chopped ginger to the stir-fry
Kapha – add ½ teaspoonful of nagkesar to the stir-fry

Saffron Lassi
(Serves Two)

Lassi is the perfect summer drink. Not only is it cooling and easily-digested, it gives you a perfect protein hit. It is best to have it at lunchtime as a part of your 'main meal' or at any time between late morning and early afternoon.

INGREDIENTS
1 cup of freshly made yoghurt
A large pinch of saffron threads
¼ cup of water
Raw jaggery to taste
Salt to taste
Crushed green cardamom

METHOD
♪ *Soak the saffron in water for twenty minutes.*
♪ *Blend the yoghurt and saffron water together. Pour into a tall glass.*
♪ *Add salt and jaggery to taste, and garnish with two strands of saffron and crushed cardamom.*

Cucumber Soup
(Serves Two)

INGREDIENTS
1 cucumber (kheera or kakdi)
½ bunch of dill
1 cup of vegetable stock
½ cup of yoghurt
A pinch of salt and black pepper
1 teaspoonful of fennel seeds (saunf)
1 tablespoonful of ghee

METHOD
♪ *Peel the cucumber and slit lengthwise. Scoop out the seeds and then chop.*
♪ *Chop the dill finely.*
♪ *Combine the vegetable stock and cucumber in a large pot.*
♪ *Purée the mixture in a food processor.*
♪ *Stir in the dill and season with salt and pepper.*

SEASONING

- *Grind the fennel seeds in a spice grinder*
- *Heat ghee in a pan, add fennel and sauté briefly*
- *Serve the soup lukewarm in a bowl and garnish with the fennel seasoning*

Raw Papaya and Turmeric Salad
(Serves Two to Three)

INGREDIENTS
1 small papaya (papita), peeled and grated
4 tablespoonsful of fresh turmeric (haldi), peeled and grated
2 tomatoes, chopped
1 green chilli
1 tablespoonful raw honey
1 tablespoonful shatavari powder
2 fresh red chillies
Salt
2 tablespoonsful of tamarind juice (imli)
4 to 5 tulsi leaves
½ cup of nuts of any kind – roasted and semi-crushed

METHOD
- *Mix the raw papaya, haldi, tomatoes, and green and red chillies in a bowl.*
- *Mix the raw honey with salt, tamarind juice. Add to the salad.*
- *Mix together the roasted nuts and shatavari powder. Add to salad and toss well.*
- *Garnish with tulsi leaves.*

Tweak for Your Dosha:
Vata and kapha – add fresh ginger to the salad
Kapha – use roasted peanuts

Coconut Flatbread

(Serves Four)

INGREDIENTS
2 cups of flour
2 cups of water
1½ cups of fresh grated coconut
Salt

METHOD
- *Mix together and roll into a soft dough. Divide into several equal parts.*
- *Using your hands, flatten each ball into a flat cake.*
- *Place roti on the tava and cook each side for at least three minutes until it turns golden-brown.*

Mint Lassi

(Serves Four)

A perfect herbal lassi for the summertime. If you prefer to have a saltier version, just replace the jaggery with salt.

INGREDIENTS
1½ cups of curds (dahi)
½ cup of mint leaves (pudina), chopped
½ teaspoonful of black salt (kala)
4 tablespoonsful of jaggery
1 teaspoonful of cumin seeds (jeera) powder
1 teaspoonful of pippali

GARNISH
A few mint leaves

METHOD
- *Combine all the ingredients in a blender and blend for two to three minutes.*
- *Add ½ a cup of water and blend again for about thirty seconds.*
- *Serve immediately in small individual glasses garnished with mint leaves.*

Tweak for Your Dosha:
Vata – add vata churna
Kapha – add kapha churna

Oat Soup
(Serves Four)

What I love about this particular soup is that you can substitute any kind of vegetables or grains depending upon whatever is in season. I have used oats and green vegetables here as these are ideal for balancing the pitta dosha, but feel free to pick and choose from the pitta list.

INGREDIENTS
½ a cup of onions, washed and chopped
3 stalks of celery, washed and chopped
1 cup of veggie 1
1 cup of veggie 2
½ a cup of oats
Salt
½ a teaspoonful of cumin
6 cups of vegetable stock
Fresh coriander or dill

METHOD
- *Combine all vegetables and water in a saucepan. Cook on low heat for about thirty minutes.*
- *Add oats and cook for another ten to fifteen minutes until the oats are cooked.*
- *Add salt and cumin.*

Tweak for Your Dosha:
Use dosha churnas to tweak for your different doshas

Sesame-Cilantro Aioli

(Serves Four to Five)

Using fresh mustard paste is ideal. However, if this is not available, you can substitute the ghee with mustard oil.

INGREDIENTS

2 garlic cloves
1 large egg yolk
2 teaspoonsful of fresh lemon juice
½ teaspoonful of mustard paste
¼ cup of extra virgin olive oil
3 tablespoonsful of ghee
1 tablespoonful of sesame seeds
1 tablespoonful of coriander, chopped

METHOD

- *Mince and mash garlic into a paste with a pinch of salt.*
- *Whisk together yolk, lemon juice and mustard in a bowl.*
- *Combine ghee and extra virgin olive oil and then add a few drops at a time to the yolk mixture, whisking constantly, until all the oil is incorporated and mixture is emulsified.*
- *If the mixture separates, stop adding oil and continue whisking until mixture comes together, then resume adding oil.*
- *Whisk in garlic paste and season with salt and pepper. If aioli is too thick, whisk in one or two drops of water.*
- *Add mustard seeds and coriander. Cover and chill until ready to use.*

Cabbage Rolls with Watercress, Dates and Mushrooms

(Serves Four to Five)

This is an Ayurvedic take on Japanese sushi rolls, but without the vinegar (which is not Ayurvedically recommended) or nori (dried seaweed) which is not too common in India. If you can find dried nori sheets from a speciality foods store, feel free to substitute them. They bring a completely different flavour to the dish.

INGREDIENTS
1 cup of shali or shastika
1 cup of water, plus extra for rinsing rice
1 tablespoonful of amla juice
1 tablespoonful of lemon juice
1 tablespoonful of jaggery
1 tablespoonful of salt
1 cup of mushrooms, chopped
½ cup of dates, chopped
1 cup of fresh watercress, chopped

METHOD
- *Place the rice into a mixing bowl and cover with cool water. Swirl the rice in the water, drain and repeat two to three times or until the water is clear.*
- *In a medium saucepan, boil the rice in water.*
- *Reduce the heat to the lowest setting and cover. Cook for fifteen minutes.*
- *Remove from the heat and let it stand covered for ten minutes.*
- *Combine the amla juice, lemon juice, sugar and salt in a small bowl.*
- *Transfer the rice into a mixing bowl and add the juice mixture.*
- *Mix thoroughly to combine and coat each grain of rice with the mixture.*
- *Cool to room temperature before using to make rolls.*
- *Sauté the mushrooms in a small amount of ghee until soft but not wilted.*
- *Take a cabbage leaf and stuff it with a small amount of rice, watercress, dates and mushrooms.*
- *Wrap the cabbage leaf with the stuffing. Hold together with a toothpick.*

Tweak for Your Dosha:
Vata – use lettuce leaves instead of cabbage
Kapha – replace mushrooms with any other vegetable from the kapha-balancing foods list

Kokum Curry
(Serves Two)

This is a wonderfully soothing anti-pitta curry that goes perfectly with plain rice and any kind of salad or whole beans dish.

INGREDIENTS
10 to 12 kokum fruits
2 cups of water
2 cups of coconut milk
Salt

SEASONING
½ teaspoonful of mustard seeds (rai)
1 teaspoonful of cumin seeds (jeera)
1 sprig of curry leaves
A pinch of asafoetida (hing)
4 to 5 garlic cloves, slightly crushed
2 kashmiri red chillies
2 tablespoonsful of ghee
Coriander leaves for garnishing

METHOD
- *Soak the kokum fruits in half a cup of water for thirty minutes. Then crush and squeeze them completely to get a pinkish-red extract.*
- *Add two cups of water to the kokum extract.*
- *Add two cups of coconut milk*
- *Add salt and stir.*
- *Heat ghee.*
- *Add mustard seeds. Keep heating until they splutter.*
- *Add cumin and let it sizzle.*
- *Add the garlic, asafoetida, red chillies, curry leaves.*
- *Top the kokum coconut milk mixture with seasoning and then with coriander leaves.*
- *Serve kokum curry straight way.*

Tulsi and Coconut Cookies
(Serves Eight)

Aside from the cooling benefits of coconut, this is a great food to munch on during snack time without the guilt of adding extra weight ... not in an unlimited supply, of course. Coconut also lowers your cholesterol levels and rejuvenates your skin. It is loaded with healthy fats and essential nutrients.

INGREDIENTS
¾ cup of almond flour
¾ cup of dried coconut meat, shredded
½ cup of date paste (dates mixed with water)
1 tablespoonful of coconut oil
1 tablespoonful of tulsi leaves, chopped
½ teaspoonful of vanilla extract
Salt to taste

METHOD
⟋ *In a food processor, combine almond flour, coconut flakes, date paste, coconut oil, tulsi, vanilla extract and salt. Mix into a slightly sticky dough.*
⟋ *Shape dough into cookie shapes of your choice and place them in the refrigerator for at least one hour to 'harden'.*

Lima Beans with Thyme and Anantamul
(Serves Four)

This wonderful dish combines the nutty flavour of lima beans with the pitta-balancing qualities of anantamul and coriander.

INGREDIENTS
2½ fresh lima beans in pods, shelled
2 teaspoonsful of extra virgin olive oil
1 small onion, minced
3 cups of anantmul decoction (dry extraction juice method)

2 teaspoonsful of fresh thyme, chopped (of you can't find this,
replace with fresh coriander leaves)
1 teaspoonful of lemon
2 teaspoonsful of honey (optional)
Salt and freshly ground black pepper

Method
- *In a saucepan, cover the beans with the anantmul decoction. Cover the pan and bring to a boil. Boil for about five to twenty minutes, depending on the size of the beans, until they are completely tender. Drain, reserving the cooking liquid.*
- *In a shallow pan, heat the olive oil. Add the onion and sauté until it changes colour.*
- *Add the drained beans and thyme and toss to coat with the oil.*
- *Then add ½ cup of the reserved cooking liquid and the lemon. Bring to a boil. Remove from the heat and season with salt and pepper to taste.*
- *Drizzle with one to two teaspoonsful of raw honey.*
- *Serve hot.*

Tweak for Your Dosha:
Vata – use ashwagandha decoction instead of anantamul
Kapha – use guggul decoction instead of anantamul

Curry Leaf Tambuli*
(Serves Two to Three)

Curry leaf tambuli is a good digestive because it has a cooling effect on the body. A great liver stimulant, it goes well with rice and can be had as a soup if prepared thin.

Ingredients
50 gm of grated coconut (nariyal)
50 gm of curry leaves (kari patta)
3 green chillies (mirchi)
10 gm of cumin seeds (jeera)

---

* Contributed by Indus Valley Ayurveda

10 seeds of pepper (mircha)
200 ml of buttermilk (chaas)
Salt (namak) to taste

SEASONING

1 teaspoonful of oil/ghee
¼ teaspoonful of mustard seeds (sarson)
A pinch of asafoetida (hing)
4 curry leaves (kari patta)

METHOD

- *Make a smooth paste of coconut, curry leaves, green chillies, cumin seeds and pepper.*
- *Add buttermilk to the ground mixture.*
- *Add salt and mix well.*

SEASONING

- *Heat oil in a pan. When oil is hot, add mustard seeds and allow to splutter, add curry leaves, asafoetida and pour the seasoning into mixture.*
- *Serve it cold or at room temperature.*

7

Vasant Ritu

MEALS TO PACIFY KAPHA ELEMENTS IN THE ENVIRONMENT

Vasant Ritu is the spring season from approximately the middle of March to the end of May. During this season, the kapha dosha is naturally aggravated and becomes liquefied by the increasing heat of the sun. This weakens agni or digestive fire. This means:

○ You are more prone to illness during this season so it is best to keep your diet light with easily digestible foods. Avoid heavy, hard-to-digest, cold-energy foods.

○ Add into your diet beverages such as fermented sugarcane juice, honey mixed with water and water boiled with extracts of sandalwood (chandan).

○ A fruit/vegetable juice fast for a few days during this season will help give your digestive system a break and rekindle your agni.

During this season, it's a good idea to undergo regular physical exercise every day and avoid taking naps during the day. While you might be able to get away with raw foods, avoid heavier meals and sweeter foods during this season. Overall, temper your foods with astringent, bitter and pungent spices to help pacify the kapha dosha in the environment. Of course, each meal can be further tweaked to meet your individual dosha type.

Breakfasts during the kapha season should be light, as should dinners. Many people can skip dinner altogether, especially if your prakruti is also dominated by the kapha dosha.

Suggested meal combinations for Vasant Ritu:

o   Watercress strawberries and radish salad, green mango smoothie

o   Sautéed bitter melon, coconut and kaala channa curry with rice and green juice 1

o   Corn soup with mix-grain khichadi, tomato chutney, cucumber-bhumyalaki juice

o   Sabudana khichadi with tomato chutney, ginger-turmeric-carrot cooler

o   Buckwheat khichadi and green juice 2

o   Citrus blaster smoothie, apple and celery salad with walnut-mustard vinaigrette

o   Snack time: kapha tea, raw almond and mustard non-cooked cookies

RECIPES

Watercress, Strawberries and Radish Salad
(Serves Four)

INGREDIENTS
1 bunch of watercress
1 cup of strawberries, halved
½ cup of radish, sliced

DRESSING
3 tablespoonsful of lemon juice
2 tablespoonsful of olive oil
Salt to taste
Black pepper
2 tablespoonsful of honey
2 cloves of garlic, crushed

METHOD
- *Wash and pluck the watercress leaves. Set aside.*
- *Combine all the ingredients for the dressing in a bowl.*
- *Halve the strawberries and slice the radish.*
- *Put watercress, radish and strawberries in a mixing bowl.*
- *Drizzle the dressing.*
- *Toss.*

Green Mango Smoothie
(Serves Two Cups)

INGREDIENTS
1½ cups of water
1 orange, peeled and roughly chopped
½ cup of fresh mango, peeled and roughly chopped
1 teaspoonful of fresh ginger, peeled and roughly chopped
1 large handful of amaranth leaves
1 small handful of fennel greens
2 stalks of celery

METHOD
- Combine the water, orange, mango and ginger in the blender.
- Blend until smooth.
- Add the celery and greens. Blend again.

Sautéed Bitter Melon
(Serves Four)

The bitter taste of karela is ideal for pacifying kapha. Many people cook karela and let it stand in salt for fifteen to thiry minutes to draw out some of the bitterness. I am generally against this idea as it is the bitter taste that is medicinal. Try it with white rice and coconut-channa curry to temper the taste.

INGREDIENTS
2 cups of bitter melon
2 tablespoonsful of ghee
1 clove garlic, crushed
½ cup fresh fenugreek leaves (methi), chopped
1 tomato, chopped
Salt
1 teaspoonful of pippali or pitta churna

METHOD
- Wash the bitter melon, then cut in half lengthwise and scoop out the seeds. Chop or slice as desired.
- Sprinkle chopped pieces with salt, then let it stand for about five to ten minutes. After standing, rinse well in cold water and then drain.
- Heat wok over medium high heat and add the oil. When the oil is hot, sauté garlic for at least thirty seconds and then add the methi. Sauté for another minute or so until the onion is translucent.
- Add the bitter melon, don't stir and cover for two minutes.
- Add the tomato stir to mix and then add pitta churna or pippali and salt.
- Cook for a further two minutes and serve with plain or fried rice.

Tweak for Your Dosha:
Vata – replace pitta churna with vata churna
Kapha – replace pitta churna with kapha churna

Coconut and Black Gram Curry
(Serves Five)

This recipe calls for cooking in a slow cooker. I particularly love slow cookers as they allow you to get maximum flavour with minimum effort. You can, of course, adjust to cook this in a large pot over very low heat. Although the recipe calls for soaked channa, I prefer sprouted kala channa if possible – this maximizes enzyme intake.

INGREDIENTS
2 teaspoonsful of ghee
½ cup of green onion, chopped
2 garlic cloves, minced
2 cups black gram (kala channa), soaked overnight
1 cup of tomatoes
2 cups of light coconut milk
1 tablespoonful of jeera
2 tablespoonsful of green chillies, chopped
Salt to taste
½ cup of fresh coriander, chopped

METHOD
- Heat a large skillet over medium heat. Add ghee and swirl to coat the pan.
- Add onion and garlic, sauté for five minutes or until green onions are tender.
- Place onion mixture, channa, tomatoes, coconut milk, jeera powder and green chillies in a slow cooker, stir well.
- Cover and cook on low heat for six to eight hours.
- Stir in coriander.
- Serve over rice.

Tweak for Your Dosha:
Vata – replace kala channa with mung beans and add vata churna
Kapha – replace kala channa with mung beans and add kapha churna

Sautéed Green Beans
(Serves Six)

INGREDIENTS
2 cups of green beans, ends chopped
1 tablespoonful of extra virgin olive oil
3 tablespoonsful of butter or ghee
2 large garlic cloves, minced
1 teaspoonful of red pepper flakes
1 tablespoonful of lemon zest
1 tablespoonful of ground pippali
Salt

METHOD
- *Blanch green beans for a few minutes in a large stockpot of well-salted boiling water, until bright green in colour and tender-crisp.*
- *Drain and replace into a bowl of ice water to stop from further cooking.*
- *Heat a large heavy skillet over medium heat. Add the oil and ghee or butter.*
- *Add the garlic and red pepper flakes and sauté until fragrant for about thirty seconds.*
- *Add the beans and continue to sauté for about five more minutes until coated in the ghee or butter and heated through.*
- *Add lemon zest and season with salt and pippali.*

Tweak for Your Dosha:
Pitta – add pitta churna

Multi-Grain Khichadi

(Serves Three to Four)

Millet is the perfect grain for balancing the kapha dosha. As such, this makes a great late winter or spring food. There are so many interesting varieties of millet in India, so you can certainly experiment with them all. Here is a multi-grain khichadi using many millets. I like to mix them all together and keep them prepared in a vat so I can easily make this khichadi at any time. If you can't find one particular variety, just drop it from the mix.

INGREDIENTS

1 cup of multi-grain mix (see below)
1 cup decoction of Triphala
2 cups of water
Salt to taste
1 tablespoonful of onions, chopped

METHOD

- *Cook the multi-grain mix in water.*
- *Sauté onions in ghee and then add the cooked mixture.*
- *Serve with green coriander and mint chutney.*

Note: *How to prepare the multi-grain mix*

1 cup of little millet (sama)
1 cup of foxtail millet (korra)
1 cup of broken ragi
1 cup of broken jowar
1 cup of broken bajra
1 cup of varagu
1 cup of broken wheat
1 cup of rice
3 cups of split green mung
3 teaspoonsful of ajwain (or as per taste)
4 teaspoonsful of sesame seeds (til)
Salt to taste

Corn Soup
(Serves Three to Four)

Corn soup is the perfect accompaniment to multi-grain khichadi. Although corn is a kharif crop in most parts of the country, it is a rabi crop in Andhra Pradesh where it is harvested in March. This soup can be blended with almond milk if you prefer a creamier texture or if you'd rather have a brothy soup with more texture, use an equal proportion of veggie stock instead.

INGREDIENTS
2 to 3 tablespoonsful of olive oil
1 cup of onion, chopped
2 cloves of garlic, minced
4 small red potatoes, quartered
Salt and black pepper
3 ears of corn, kernels sliced off
2 cups of vegetable stock
2 cups of almond milk
2 to 3 green onions, chopped
½ teaspoonful of red chilli powder
1 teaspoonful of tulsi leaves, chopped

METHOD
- *In a large saucepan over medium heat, add olive oil, onion and garlic and sauté for three to four minutes.*
- *Add potato, season with a little salt and pepper, and cover to steam for four to five minutes.*
- *Add most of the corn, reserving a little for garnish, and stir.*
- *If you plan to blend the soup, add half the broth, half the almond milk for a creamier texture. If you intend to leave it unblended, just use broth for best results.*
- *Add broth and almond milk (if blending only), cover, and bring to a low boil. Reduce heat to low.*
- *Cook until the potatoes are soft, for about five minutes.*

- If blending, add ¾ of the soup to a blender and blend until creamy and smooth.
- Transfer soup back to the saucepan and bring back to a simmer. Taste and adjust seasoning as needed.
- Cook for at least ten minutes and allow to thicken. The longer it simmers, the more flavourful it will be.
- To serve – top with chopped green onion, tulsi, red chilli, remaining fresh (or lightly sautéed) corn and black pepper. Add a few red chillies also for colour.
- Serve with multi-grain khichadi and coriander chutney.

Cucumber-Bhumyalaki Juice with Ginger

(Serves Two)

INGREDIENTS
2 cups of cucumber, chopped
1-inch piece of fresh ginger, chopped
½ cup of bhumyalaki swaras

METHOD
- Blend both together.
- Strain and serve.

Buckwheat Khichadi

(Serves Two to Three)

This khichadi is made with buckwheat groats (sabut kuttu), potatoes and peanuts. An ideal springtime dish made with a wholesome super food.

INGREDIENTS
1 cup of buckwheat or buckwheat groats (sabut kuttu)
2 medium potatoes, chopped into small cubes
2 cups of water
1 green chilli, chopped
½-inch ginger, finely chopped
½ teaspoonful of cumin seeds (jeera)

1 teaspoonful of jaggery
2 tablespoonsful of raw peanuts
1 tablespoonful of ghee
1 tablespoonful of coriander leaves, chopped
Lemon juice as required (optional)
Rock salt to taste

METHOD

- In a frying pan or tava, roast peanuts until they become crunchy and golden.
- When peanuts have cooled, grind them into a coarse powder using a mortar-pestle.
- Rinse the buckwheat in water and set aside.
- Heat ghee or oil in a pan or pot.
- Add cumin seeds and sauté till they splutter.
- Add green chilli and ginger and sauté for a few seconds.
- Add potato cubes and sauté for two to three minutes until the potatoes become crisp at the edges. Stir well.
- Add the ground peanuts and sauté. Then add the rinsed buckwheat. Stir well and sauté for one to two minutes.
- Add the water, jaggery and salt.
- Stir and cover the pan and allow the buckwheat to simmer on a low flame. Cook until all the water is absorbed and the buckwheat has cooked well.
- Add coriander leaves and give a final stir.
- Serve buckwheat khichadi hot or warm, drizzled with lemon juice.

Tweak for Your Dosha:
Vata – replace buckwheat with whole wheat

Ginger-Turmeric-Carrot Cooler
(Serves Two)

INGREDIENTS
¼-inch piece of fresh turmeric
2-inch piece of ginger
4 celery stalks
3 carrots

1 cucumber
1 lemon

METHOD
- *Wash all vegetables thoroughly.*
- *Juice each vegetable in this order – turmeric, celery, carrots, lemon, cucumber, ginger, turmeric.*
- *Stir mixture before serving.*

Homemade Tomato Chutney
(Serves Four to Six)

This wonderful chutney is ideal for both winter and spring. It goes with just about anything – rice, chapattis, idli and dosa.

INGREDIENTS
6 tomatoes
2 onions
2 green chillies
2 teaspoonsful of red chilli powder
2 teaspoonsful of garlic
Pinch of turmeric
½ teaspoonful of cumin seeds
1 teaspoonful of mustard seeds
Curry leaves
2 teaspoonsful of ghee

METHOD
- *Heat ghee and splutter mustard seeds.*
- *Add jeera.*
- *Add garlic.*
- *Add onion.*
- *Add green chillies.*
- *Add curry leaves.*
- *Sauté until the onion changes colour.*
- *Add tomatoes.*
- *Add chilli powder, turmeric and salt.*
- *Cover with a lid, simmer for five minutes.*

- ◢ *Remove lid, mash tomatoes, cook for another five minutes.*
- ◢ *Add a little water and bring to a boil.*
- ◢ *Remove from heat.*

Tweak for Your Dosha:
Pitta – replace with another chutney

Tapioca (Sabudana) Khichadi
(Serves Two to Three)

Sabudana khichadi is a very popular Maharashtrian dish prepared with soaked sabudana, potatoes and roasted peanut powder. It is popularly eaten during the Navratri fast which happens during this season. However, if you are fasting, skip the curry leaves and mustard seeds (these are not traditionally taboo during the fast).

INGREDIENTS
1 cup of tapioca (sabudana)
2 potatoes (boiled)
½ cup of roasted peanuts (skinned)
1 tablespoonful (andaaze se) of mustard oil
1 teaspoonful of mustard seeds
1 teaspoonful of cumin seeds (jeera)
2 green chillies
4 to 5 curry leaves
1 teaspoonful of jaggery
2 tablespoonsful of coconut (grated)
1 tablespoonful of lemon juice
Salt

METHOD
- ◢ *Wash one cup of sabudana in water and soak it in water for thirty minutes. Drain the water and let the tapioca stand for approximately six to eight hours.*
- ◢ *Chop the roasted peanuts coarsely.*
- ◢ *Cut the boiled potatoes into small cubes.*

⟡ *Heat mustard oil in a pan and add mustard seeds. When they splutter, add the jeera, green chillies and curry leaves.*

⟡ *Add the potatoes, salt, jaggery and mix well.*

⟡ *Add the sabudana, mix well and cook on a low flame for five minutes.*

⟡ *Add the peanut powder and the coconut. Cook for one minute.*

⟡ *Squeeze lemon juice over mixture.*

Tweak for Your Dosha:
Pitta – replace peanuts with pumpkin seeds

Green Juice # 1
(Serves Two)

INGREDIENTS
2 sweet apples
1 large cucumber
1 small lime
2 handfuls of leafy greens (or cabbage, chopped broccoli, basella leaves, mustard greens, etc.)
1 handful of coriander, with stems
½ cup of chitrak swaras

METHOD
⟡ *Add apple, cucumber, lime, greens and coriander to your juicer.*

⟡ *Add chitrak swaras to the blend.*

⟡ *Pour into a glass and enjoy!*

Tweak for Your Dosha:
Replace chitrak swaras with swaras of any other herb that balances your dosha

Green Juice # 2
(Serves Two)

INGREDIENTS
1 cucumber, chopped
½ lemon or lime, chopped

2 stalks of celery, chopped
2 stalks of Chinese spinach (chauli or chavleri saag)
½ cup of punarnava swaras
½–1 inch piece of ginger
Extra water

METHOD

⟆ *Add cucumber, lime, celery, spinach, ginger and water to your juicer.*
⟆ *Add punarnava swaras to the blend.*
⟆ *Pour into a glass and enjoy!*

Tweak for Your Dosha:

Replace punarnava swaras with swaras of any other herb that balances your dosha

Raw Almond and Mustard Cookies
(Serves Four to Six Pieces)

These savoury cookies make an ideal munchie for kapha-balancing.

INGREDIENTS

½ cup of whole almonds
½ cup of oat flour
1 tablespoonful of fresh mustard paste
2 tablespoonsful of finely shredded coconut
1 tablespoonful of psyllium husk
1 tablespoonful of virgin coconut oil
1 teaspoonful of pure vanilla extract
A small pinch of Himalayan/sea salt
2 teaspoonsful of mustard leaves, chopped

METHOD

⟆ *Combine all the ingredients, except the mustard leaves, in the blender and blend until it becomes a sticky mixture with not a lot of big pieces remaining.*
⟆ *Spoon the mixture into a bowl.*
⟆ *Add the chopped mustard leaves and stir it around for little while.*

- *Fill a large round spoon or small ice cream scoop with the mix and press down so it can become the shape of a cookie.*
- *Repeat with the rest of the cookie dough.*

Apple and Celery Salad with Walnut-Mustard Vinaigrette
(Serves Two to Three)

INGREDIENTS
¼ cup of fresh lemon juice
¼ cup of fresh mustard paste
5 teaspoonsful of honey
²/₃ cup of extra virgin olive oil
1 large bunch of celery with leaves
2 large apples, cut into wedges
¾ cup of raw walnuts, chopped

METHOD
FOR VINAIGRETTE
- *In a small bowl, blend first three ingredients.*
- *Gradually whisk in oil.*
- *Season with salt and pepper.*

FOR SALAD
- *Trim celery leaves and chop enough to measure one cup.*
- *Thinly slice stalks on deep diagonal.*
- *In a large bowl, combine celery stalks, celery leaves, apples and walnuts.*
- *Add vinaigrette and toss to coat.*
- *Season salad to taste with salt and pepper.*

Citrus Juice Blaster
(Serves Two)

This refreshing juice blend is perfect for spring-time detoxifying and cleansing. High in fibre, antioxidants and vitamins, it is also the perfect metabolic booster.

INGREDIENTS

2 grapefruit

4 oranges

2 lemons

½ teaspoonful of red chilli

METHOD

⸆ Peel the oranges and grapefruit.

⸆ Juice them in a juice machine or a citrus press.

⸆ Juice the lemon along with the rind if possible.

⸆ Mix all ingredients together.

Ridgegourd Payasa*

(Serves Four)

This is a delicious dessert, ideal for balancing kapha dosha.

INGREDIENTS

¼ kg of ridge gourd (thoori)

½ litre of milk

2 tablespoonful of ghee

5 tablespoonful of rice

½ cup of sugar

10 almonds

10 cashews

25 raisins

3 cardamoms

METHOD:

⸆ Peel the ridge gourd and grate it.

⸆ Soak the rice in water for ten minutes.

⸆ Boil the milk, add grated ridge gourd and let it boil for another ten minutes.

⸆ Grind the soaked rice to a fine paste by adding required amount of water along with almonds and cashews (leaving two almonds and two cashews for garnishing).

---

* Contributed by Indus Valley Ayurveda

- *Add the ground rice paste slowly while stirring continuously and let it boil until it becomes thick.*
- *Reduce the flame and add sugar, cardamom powder and give the mixture a good stir.*
- *Cut the remaining almonds and cashews into pieces and fry in ghee along with the raisins until it turns golden-brown, keep aside.*
- *Switch off the flame and add the roasted nuts along with ghee to your delicious payasa.*

8

Hemant Ritu and Shishir Ritu

MEALS TO PACIFY VATA AND KAPHA ELEMENTS IN THE ENVIRONMENT

Hemant Ritu is the early part of the winter from about mid-November to mid-January. Shishir Ritu is the latter part of the winter from about mid-January to mid-March. During these seasons, your digestive activity becomes more powerful. The vata dosha increases, but can become obstructed from spreading outwards because of the cold atmosphere around. The kapha dosha also increases during Hemant Ritu and becomes aggravated during Shishir Ritu. The actions of increased vata and kapha, individually or together, can negatively impact the dhaatus. Therefore, a higher intake of vata-balancing foods, especially during the early part of the winter, and kapha herbs, especially during the latter part of the winter, is ideal.

During this season, it's a good idea to undergo regular oil massages and ubtan treatments. Regular physical exercise is an absolute must as is exposure to the winter sunlight if possible.

Breakfasts during this season should be light, as should dinners. Of course, each meal can be further tweaked to meet your individual dosha type.

Suggested meals for Hemant Ritu:
○ Upma (cracked wheat) with sesame chutney and herbed carrots
○ Urad dal with saffron rice, zucchini fritters
○ Slow-cooked sweet potato, apples and caramelized onions, sautéed bottle gourd with mustard greens, red rice or millet
○ Root vegetable ragout, barley and ginger with turmeric swaras
○ Vata snack time: seasonal tea and nachani laddoo cookies

Suggested meal combinations for Shishir Ritu:
○ Mustard and turnip greens, corn bread with home-made butter and haldi swaras or kanji
○ Poha cutlets with spiced cabbage, buttermilk and green mango chutney with haldi and ajmoda swaras
○ Fenugreek and radish curry with ragi roti or rice, cabbage chutney with kanji
○ Spiced millet with carrot and turmeric chutney with ginger and mint swaras
○ Snack time: Triphala tea with raw almond and mustard non-cooked cookies

RECIPES

Root Vegetable Ragout
(Serves Two)

INGREDIENTS
1 cup of onions, cut into wedges
1 medium turnip (shalgam)
2 carrots
½ cup of beetroots (chukandar)
1 teaspoonful of ghee
1 teaspoonful of mustard oil
2 tablespoonsful of unsalted butter (safed makkhan)
½ cup of vegetable stock
Parsley leaves (for garnishing)
Grated lemon zest (for garnishing)

METHOD
- *Preheat oven to 425°F.*
- *Peel vegetables, cut enough into ½-inch cubes to measure ¾ cup each.*
- *In a shallow roasting pan, toss vegetables (except onions) with mustard oil and ghee mix. Roast in middle of oven until tender and golden, for about twenty minutes.*
- *In a large skillet, heat ghee over moderate flame and then cook onions, stirring until tender and pale golden.*
- *Add roasted vegetables, veggie stock and salt and pepper to taste and simmer for about two minutes until stock is slightly thickened and coats vegetables.*
- *Sprinkle kapha churna over the vegetables.*
- *Garnish with parsley and zest.*

Tweak for Your Dosha:
Switch the churna to suit your dosha

Nachani and Date Laddoos
(Serves Five)

Nachani and date laddoos are sweet, cooling and slightly heavy to digest. They are best had in the daylight hours as an afternoon snack.

INGREDIENTS
1 cup of millet flour (nachani)
1 cup of dates, seeded and finely chopped
2 teaspoonsful of poppy or sesame seeds
¼ teaspoonful of ground cardamom
5 tablespoonsful of ghee

METHOD
- *Heat three tablespoonsful of ghee in a pan over medium heat.*
- *Add the millet flour and cook, stirring continuously until the flour turns golden-brown.*
- *Remove from heat and transfer to a mixing bowl.*
- *Dry roast the poppy or sesame seeds in the same pan and then add to the mixing bowl.*
- *Heat the remaining two tablespoonsful of ghee over medium heat, add the dates, sauté for two minutes and transfer to the mixing bowl.*
- *Add ground cardamom and knead together until the flour and date mixture is mixed well and while it is still warm, divide it into smaller, equal parts.*
- *Take a little ghee in your hands and shape each portion into round laddoos.*

Tweak for Your Dosha:
Kapha – replace nachani with rye

Sesame Chutney
(Serves Two to Three)

INGREDIENTS
3 tablespoonsful of white sesame seeds (til)
2 tablespoonsful of melon seeds (magaj), soaked in water for three to four hours
1 tablespoonful of poppy seeds (khuskhus), soaked in water for three to four hours
5 to 6 garlic cloves
½-inch ginger, chopped
1 tablespoonful of cumin seeds
1 tablespoonful of pippali
1 teaspoonful of asafoetida (hing)
4 tablespoonsful of desiccated coconut
1 teaspoonful of jaggery
1 teaspoonful of turmeric
1 tablespoonful of red chilli powder
7 to 8 curry leaves
1 teaspoonful of fennel seed powder
Salt

METHOD
- *Soak sesame seeds, melon seeds and poppy seeds in water for three to four hours.*
- *Combine everything into a processor. Grind to a smooth paste.*
- *Store in refrigerator. You can store it for upto five to seven days.*

Tweak for Your Dosha:
Kapha – add green chillies if you want it spicier
Pitta – replace hing with an equal quantity of sesame and watermelon seeds

Upma (Cracked Wheat)
(Serves Five to Six)

INGREDIENTS
1 cup of semolina (rava)
1 cup of ghee
½ teaspoonful of mustard seeds
1 teaspoonful of almonds, peeled and chopped
1 teaspoonful of fresh pippali, chopped
3 to 4 fresh brahmi leaves
1 teaspoonful of fresh ashwagndha root, chopped (or ½ teaspoonful of dried ashwagandha)
1 teaspoonful of cumin
½ teaspoonful of ginger, grated
3 to 5 medium chillies, chopped
1 medium onion
Salt
¾ cup vegetables – peas, carrots, tomatoes, green peppers, broccoli, zucchini, okra (or other veggies) – any of these or a mix of them
3 tablespoonsful of fresh coconut meat, grated – this is optional
2 teaspoonsful of freshly squeezed lemon juice

METHOD
- Dry roast the semolina until it turns brown.
- In a large saucepan, heat the ghee.
- Add mustard seeds. When it sputters, add cumin, ginger, green chillies, onions, almonds, pippali, brahmi leaf, ashwagandha root. Stir until the onions caramelize.
- Add vegetables, salt and two cups of water. Bring to a boil.
- Add roasted semolina (rava), turn down the heat and mix until the semolina absorbs all the water.
- Garnish with coconut and coriander leaves. Squeeze lemon juice on top.

Tweak for Your Dosha:
Pitta – replace ashwagandha with fennel leaves
Kapha – replace ashwagandha and brahmi with tulsi leaves

Herbed Carrots
(Serves Two)

INGREDIENTS
2 bunches of baby carrots, cleaned, peeled (or 3 to 4 regular-sized carrots, cleaned, peeled and sliced)
2 teaspoonsful of olive oil
Salt
Ground black pepper
I tablespoonful of ghee
2 teaspoonsful of fresh mustard paste
I tablespoonful of fresh herbs, chopped (dill, green onions, coriander, etc.)

METHOD
- *Heat oven to 450°F.*
- *Place the carrots on a baking sheet, drizzle with the oil, season with salt and pepper, and toss to evenly coat.*
- *Roast, shaking the pan occasionally, until a knife easily pierces the carrots, for about ten to fifteen minutes. Smaller carrots will cook in less time. Remove from the oven and set aside.*
- *Melt ghee in a large frying pan.*
- *Add mustard and stir to combine.*
- *Add the roasted carrots and herbs and toss to coat the carrots in the butter mixture.*
- *Season with salt and pepper.*

Tweak for Your Dosha:
Pitta – replace mustard with aloe vera juice

Sweet Potatoes, Apples and Onions, Slow Cooked with Spices and then topped with Flax Seed
(Serves Four to Six)

Sweet potatoes slow cooked with apples and spices makes for a healthy dish perfect for the winter.

INGREDIENTS

2 sweet potatoes, sliced or chopped
2 apples, chopped
1 onion
¼ cup of jaggery
2 tablespoonsful of ghee, melted
¼ teaspoonful of cinnamon
½ teaspoonful of vata churna
Salt and pepper to taste

METHOD

- *Cube sweet potatoes and apples and place them in a slow cooker.*
- *Sprinkle remaining ingredients on top of the potatoes and apples.*
- *Cook on low for four to five hours.*
- *Add salt and pepper to taste.*
- *Garnish with flax seed*

Tweak for Your Dosha:
Replace churna with pitta or kapha churna.

Sautéed Lauki and Braised Mustard Greens

(Serves Four)

INGREDIENTS

1 tablespoonful of olive oil
1 cup of bottle gourd (laubi)
½ medium onion, chopped
1 tablespoonful of celery, minced
1 teaspoonful of garlic, minced
½ teaspoonful of ginger, minced
1 green chilli, sliced
4 to 5 curry leaves
A few capers
4 cherry tomatoes, halved
2 black olives
1 cup of mustard greens, braised and cut
Juice of ½ a lemon

1 teaspoonful of sesame seeds
5 to 6 tulsi leaves, chopped
Salt and pepper to taste

METHOD

- ♪ Wash and dry the lauki, cut and trim away the pith and slice into chunky bite-sized pieces.
- ♪ Sweat the onions and celery in olive oil for a couple of minutes.
- ♪ Pour a few tablespoonful of oil into the pan and let it heat for a minute. Transfer the onions and celery to the pan.
- ♪ Add a pinch of salt which will help draw the liquid out of the onions.
- ♪ Stir the onions around until all the pieces are thinly coated with oil and evenly distributed in the pan.
- ♪ Cover the pan with a lid or aluminium foil to trap the moisture and prevent the onions from browning.
- ♪ Stir the onions around once a minute.
- ♪ Turn the heat down to low if the onions start to brown. They will start to sweat after a few minutes of cooking.
- ♪ Add the minced ginger, garlic and the minced chillies.
- ♪ Add the slices of bottle gourd and roast in the pan.
- ♪ Add the mustard greens, curry leaves and olives and continue to toss well.
- ♪ Add the cherry tomatoes, a dash of lemon juice and some freshly chopped tulsi leaves and sesame seeds.
- ♪ Serve with bulgur wheat, red rice or millet and a dosha tea of your choice.

Zucchini Fritters

(Serves Four to Five)

INGREDIENTS

2 medium zucchinis
1 teaspoonful of coarse salt
2 green onions, split lengthwise and thinly sliced
1 large egg, lightly beaten
Freshly ground black pepper
½ cup of rava or wheat

½ teaspoon of baking powder
Ghee

TOPPING
1 cup of yoghurt (dahi)
1 to 2 tablespoonsful of lemon juice
¼ teaspoonful of lemon zest
A pinch of salt
1 small clove of garlic, minced or crushed

METHOD
- *Preheat oven to 200°F.*
- *Trim ends off zucchini and grate or shred them in a food processor.*
- *In a large bowl, toss zucchini with one teaspoonful of salt and set aside for ten minutes.*
- *Wring out the zucchini by pressing it against the holes of a colander with a wooden spoon to extract the water or squeezing out small handfuls at a time.*
- *Return zucchini shreds to a bowl.*
- *Add scallions, egg and some freshly-ground black pepper and a little more salt if necessary.*
- *Separately, stir together the flour and baking powder, then stir the mixture into the zucchini batter.*
- *In a large tava, heat two teaspoonsful of ghee.*
- *Drop small bunches of the zucchini mixture onto the tava only a few at a time so they don't become crowded and lightly flatten them with the back of your spatula.*
- *Cook fritters over medium heat until the edges underneath are golden, for about three to four minutes.*
- *Flip the fritters and fry them on the other side until browned underneath again, for about two to three minutes more.*
- *Drain briefly on paper towels, then transfer to baking sheet and then keep warm in the oven until it's time to serve the dish.*
- *For the topping, stir together the dahi, lemon juice, zest, salt and garlic and adjust the flavours to your taste.*
- *Place a dollop of the topping on each fritter before serving.*

Tweak for Your Dosha:
Pitta and kapha – instead of frying, bake the fritters through and
through.

Bulgur Wheat

(Serves Six)

INGREDIENTS

1 cup of bulgur wheat
½ cup of green olives, pitted
½ small red onion, sliced
⅓ cup of currants or raisins
⅓ cup of flat-leaf parsley, chopped
½ cup of fresh coriander leaves, chopped,
¼ cup of pistachios, raw and lightly crushed
2 tablespoonsful of fresh lemon juice
Freshly-ground black pepper

METHOD

- *In a large bowl, soak bulgur with 1½ cups of boiling water for forty-five minutes until it has softened and all the water is absorbed.*
- *Add olives, onion, currants, parsley, coriander, pistachios and lemon juice.*
- *Season to taste with salt and pepper.*
- *Let the mixture stand for at least thirty minutes for flavours to mix.*
- *Sprinkle with more chopped coriander and drizzle with oil.*

Tweak for Your Dosha:
Pitta – add 1 tablespoonful of rosewater to the salad
Kapha – add mint leaves

Urad Dal Soup

(Serves Four to Six)

INGREDIENTS

3 cups of urad dal, skinned and split, cooked
3 tablespoonsful of chana dal, cooked
½ medium onion, finely chopped
½ fresh green chilli, chopped
3 cloves of garlic, minced
½ teaspoonful of black mustard seeds
¼ teaspoonful of red chilli powder
½ teaspoonful of turmeric powder
¾ to 1 teaspoonful of salt
A pinch of asafoetida (hing)
¼ cup of fresh coriander leaves with extra for garnish, finely chopped
1½ tablespoonsful of ghee
2 cups water

METHOD

- *In a large pot, heat ghee.*
- *Add black mustard seeds and asafoetida and fry for a few seconds until fragrant.*
- *Add garlic, onions, and green chilli. Sauté until fragrant and the onions start to become translucent.*
- *Add the cooked urad dal, cooked chana dal, turmeric powder and salt. Sauté with the onion-garlic mixture for a few minutes, mixing frequently.*
- *Add water and bring the soup to a gentle simmer. Once simmering, turn down the heat to medium-low.*
- *Continue to simmer on low heat until some of the water boils off and the soup becomes thick, for about ten to twenty minutes.*
- *Garnish with chopped coriander.*

Tweak for Your Dosha:

Pitta – add rosewater and rose petal garnish
Kapha – add freshly chopped ginger and tulsi leaves into the seasoning mix

Slow-Cooked Mustard and Turnip Greens with Cornbread

(Serves Five)

This is my western take on the north Indian winter staple, Sarson ka Saag and Makki di roti. Made in a slow cooker, it becomes very easy to prepare. The longer the greens cook, the better the flavour

INGREDIENTS

2 bunches of fresh mustard greens (4 lbs)
3 turnips, peeled and cut into quarters
I cup of vegetable stock
I tablespoon of jaggery
½ teaspoonful of turmeric
2-inch ginger, chopped
2 green chillies, chopped
7 to 8 garlic cloves, chopped
½ teaspoonful of red chilli powder
A pinch of asafoetida
Salt as required

METHOD

⟡ Fill clean sink about halfway with lukewarm water. Chop turnip greens and place into the sink to clean. Agitate the water and turnip greens with your hands to dislodge any dirt and grit from the turnip greens. Drain water and repeat until the greens are clean.

⟡ Add half of the greens to the slow cooker with about one cup of vegetable stock, peeled and quartered turnips, jaggery, ginger and garlic and red chilli powder (optional).

⟡ Cook on low setting for about one hour until the greens have reduced. Add remaining greens to the slow cooker and set time on low for four more hours.

Hemant Ritu meal:
root vegetable ragout,
barley and ginger with
turmeric swaras

> Cold pea soup with rosewater, okra, pomegranate and coconut salad, barley khichadi with sunflower sprouts

Suggested meal combinations for Sharad Ritu (Autumn: September–November)

> Saffron lassi, coconut flatbread and lima beans with thyme and anantamul, arugula and mung dal salad

> Sautéed bean sprouts with coriander chutney, plain rice and cucumber soup

🌿 Sautéed bitter melon with coconut, black gram curry with rice and green juice

🌿 Tapioca khichidi with tomato chutney, ginger-turmuric-carrot cooler

Suggested meal combinations for Vasant Ritu (Spring: March–May)

🌿 Watercress, strawberries and radish salad, green mango smoothie

🦋 Urad dal soup with saffron rice and zucchini fritters

Suggested meal combinations for Hemant Ritu (early Winter: November-January)

🦋 Upma with sesame chutney, and herbed carrots

🦋 Slow-cooked sweet potato, apples and caramelized onions, sautéed bottle gourd with mustard greens, and red rice

🌿 Mustard & turnip greens, corn bread with home-made butter and kanji

🌿 Poha cutlets with spiced cabbage, buttermilk, green mango chutney with haldi and ajmoda swaras

Suggested meal combinations for Shishir Ritu (late Winter: January–March)

🌿 Fenugreek and radish curry with ragi roti, cabbage chutney and kanji

🌿 Pumpkin dal soup
with dashmul dressing
and amla sherbet

Suggested meal combinations for
Grishma Ritu (Summer: May-July)

🌿 Plantain slices topped with
a spicy dressing and puris

🌿 Stuffed okra with roti
and kesar-pista lassi

❦ Banana-cucumber salad
and oat soup

❦ Turmeric and ginger swaras
with honey

Suggested meal combinations for
Varsha Ritu (Monsoon: July-September)

❦ Dal kebabs with
sautéed bean sprouts

Vata snack time: Raspberry-refresher smoothie and Chyawanprash cookies

Buttermilk Cornbread
(Serves Eight)

Try this for a change instead of the usual makki ki roti.

INGREDIENTS
Ghee
2 cups of cornmeal
1 cup of dhokla flour
1 tablespoon of bicarbonate of soda
2 eggs
2 cups of buttermilk
½ cup of water

METHOD
- Preheat oven to 425°F.
- Coat large skillet with ghee and place in oven. Remove skillet from oven once the ghee has melted.
- Mix all the ingredients together and pour into the hot grease in the skillet. Return to the oven and bake for about ten to fifteen minutes or until the bread has risen and the centre springs to the touch.
- Serve directly from skillet or allow to stand for about five minutes and flip onto a plate for serving.

Carrot Kanji
(Serves Eight cups)

This traditional Punjabi fermented drink is made in the winters with black carrots. As a probiotic, it is excellent for digestion. If you cannot find black carrots, use regular carrots and add beetroot to give extra colour.

INGREDIENTS
5 to 6 medium-sized carrots (kaala gajar)
2 small beetroots
8 cups of water, boiled and filtered
1½ teaspoonful of red chilli powder

3 tablespoonsful of mustard powder
Black salt for taste

METHOD

- *Rinse and peel the carrots and beetroots.*
- *Chop into long pieces.*
- *In a glass or ceramic jar, mix all the ingredients.*
- *Cover with a lid or muslin cloth and keep the jar in the sun for three to four days.*
- *Stir with a clean wooden spoon every day before returning the jars to the sun.*
- *When the kanji tastes sour, the drink is fermented.*
- *Serve carrot kanji immediately.*

Fenugreek and Radish Curry

(Serves Four)

Here is a great late-winter veggie dish. Besan and garlic give it a unique flavour.

INGREDIENTS

1 bunch of fresh fenugreek (methi) leaves
7 to 8 red radishes, chopped into quarters
2 cloves of garlic, chopped
1 tablespoonful of besan flour
Salt to taste
A pinch of jaggery
½ teaspoonful of turmeric
½ teaspoonful of chilli powder
½ teaspoonful of jeera seeds
1 tablespoonful of ghee
1 tomato, chopped (optional)

METHOD

- *Heat the oil in a pan, add jeera until it sizzles.*
- *Add the garlic cloves and the radishes.*
- *Add a little bit of water to cook the radishes halfway through.*
- *Add the besan flour and stir until it is a bit golden-brown.*

- Add the methi leaves and the seasonings.
- Simmer on low heat, but be careful not to burn and add a little bit of water if it seems too dry.
- Add tomatoes for more depth of flavour.
- Serve warm with chapattis or with rice and yoghurt.

Ragi Roti
(Serves Four)

This protein-rich roti, made without any oil, is perfect for the winters.

INGREDIENTS
½ cup of ragi (nachani or red millet) flour
3 tablespoonsful of spring onions, finely chopped (green and white part)
¼ cup of carrot, grated
1½ tablespoonsful of yoghurt (dahi)
½ teaspoonful of green chilli paste
Salt

METHOD
- In a bowl, combine all the ingredients with water and knead into a smooth dough.
- Divide the dough into four equal portions.
- Roll each portion out into a roti.
- Place the roti on a non-stick pan. Turn over in a few seconds.
- Cook the other side for a few more seconds.
- Lift the roti with a pair of flat tongs and roast over an open flame until brown spots appear on both the sides.
- Repeat with the remaining portions to make remaining rotis.
- Serve hot.

Cabbage Chutney
(Serves Two to Three)

INGREDIENTS
1 cup of cabbage, shredded or chopped
½ cup of onions, chopped
½-inch piece of ginger
2 green chillies
½ cup of tomato, chopped
A few curry leaves
¼ teaspoonful of tamarind
1 tablespoonful of grated coconut

SEASONING
2 teaspoonsful of mustard oil
½ teaspoonful of mustard seeds
2 teaspoonsful of urad dal
1 red chilli
A pinch of asafoetida (hing)

METHOD
- *Chop all the vegetables.*
- *In a kadai, heat oil and add mustard seeds. When they splutter, add urad dal, red chillies and hing.*
- *Sauté until dal turns golden-brown.*
- *Remove from pan.*
- *In the same kadai, add chopped onions, ginger, green chilli, a few curry leaves and sauté until onions turn translucent.*
- *Add cabbage and cook until the raw smell of the cabbage dissipates.*
- *Add tomatoes and cook for a few more minutes.*
- *Let the mixture cool.*
- *Grind the urad dal and red chilli into a fine paste. Add a little of the cabbage mixture and grind together.*
- *Add remaining cooked cabbage mixture, tamarind paste, grated coconut and grind it well, adding salt to taste.*
- *Heat another teaspoonful of oil, add ½ teaspoonful mustard seeds, when it splutters, add curry leaves and pour it over the cabbage chutney.*

Tweak for Your Dosha:
Add one teaspoonful of the relevant dosha churna to the mix

Spiced Millet Salad
(Serves Six to Eight)

INGREDIENTS
2 cups of cooked millet (varagu, thinai, bajra or ragi)
I medium eggplant, cubed
¼ red bell pepper, diced
2 cups of chickpeas or chickpea sprouts, soaked
½ cup of raisins
I cup of arugula, chopped
¼ cup of walnuts or almonds
I teaspoonful of garam masala
I tablespoonful of fresh turmeric, chopped
½ teaspoonful of cinnamon
Salt to taste
Black pepper and cayenne to taste
I teaspoonful of extra virgin olive oil
I teaspoonful of ghee

METHOD
- *Sauté the eggplant in ghee.*
- *Mix all the ingredients together.*
- *Let it sit for at least an hour in the fridge to cool for the flavours to absorb.*

Tweak for Your Dosha:
Pitta – leave the eggplant raw
Vata – sauté eggplant and bell pepper

Carrot and Turmeric Chutney
(Serves Two Cups)

Carrot chutney is a simple, healthy way to eat root vegetables. You can even use it as a spread for a sandwich.

INGREDIENTS

1 cup of carrot, grated
¼ cup of coconut, grated
½ to ¾ cup of fresh turmeric, grated
1½ tablespoonsful of urad dal
5 to 6 red chillies
1 small tamarind
1 teaspoonful of mustard oil
Salt
Coriander leaves, chopped for garnish

METHOD

- *In a pan, heat oil and fry the urad dal and red chillies until they turn golden-brown.*
- *Add the turmeric and grated carrots. Sauté the grated carrots until the raw smell disappears.*
- *Transfer the sautéed items into a food processor or mixer and grind with coconut, tamarind, salt and water into a smooth chutney.*
- *Top with chopped coriander.*

Poha Cutlets

(Makes Ten Cutlets)

INGREDIENTS

1 cup of poha/flattened rice
2 potatoes, boiled and mashed
½ cup of cheddar cheese, grated
2 medium green chillies, finely chopped
1 teaspoonful of kapha churna
1 teaspoonful of chilli flakes
½ teaspoonful of amchoor powder
½ teaspoonful of rock salt (kala namak)
Black pepper and salt to taste
½ cup of fresh coriander leaves, roughly chopped
2 tablespoonsful of corn flour
1 cup of bread crumbs
Water

METHOD

- *Soak poha in water for ten minutes, add just as much water as needed to cover the poha completely.*
- *When the poha turns soft and a little mushy, discard any excess water.*
- *Add all the other ingredients, except corn flour and breadcrumbs. Combine with your hands to make a thick dough-like mixture.*
- *Mix corn flour with ¼ cup of water. Adjust the quantity of water to make a runny liquid to crumb coat the cutlets.*
- *Heat oil for deep frying.*
- *Divide the dough into equal portions and roll out flat cutlets.*
- *Dip cutlets in the corn flour liquid and then coat them with bread crumbs.*
- *Pre-heat oven to 375°F and keep a tray ready, lined with parchment paper.*
- *Place cutlets on a baking sheet and bake until golden-brown on one side, which takes about fifteen minutes. Then flip to the other side and bake again for another ten minutes.*
- *Serve with chutney.*

Tweak for Your Dosha:

Vata – replace kapha churna with vata churna

Pitta – Replace kapha churna with pitta churna; remove chilli flakes

Spiced Cabbage

(Serves Four)

INGREDIENTS

1 teaspoonful of chilli powder

1 teaspoonful of dried thyme

1 teaspoonful of smoked red chilli

1 teaspoonful of dried oregano

½ teaspoonful of ground cumin

½ teaspoonful of dosha churna

1 teaspoonful of salt

2 tablespoonsful of butter

1 small onion, sliced
3 cloves of garlic, minced
1 small head cabbage, finely shredded

METHOD

- *Combine chilli powder, thyme, oregano, cumin and salt in a bowl.*
- *Melt butter in a large skillet over medium heat.*
- *Cook and stir onion in hot butter until translucent, for about five minutes.*
- *Add garlic and cook until soft, for about two minutes.*
- *Stir shredded cabbage into onion and garlic. Cook and stir cabbage mixture until cabbage starts to soften, for about five minutes.*
- *Stir spices into cabbage mixture and cook, stirring often until spices are evenly mixed in and cabbage is tender, for about three minutes.*

Tweak for Your Dosha:
Change churna as necessary

Green Mango Chutney
(Serves One Small Cup)

INGREDIENTS

2 small or 1 medium sized mango, peeled & chopped
1 cup of fresh coconut meat
1 or 2 green chillies
1 or 2 garlic cloves (optional)
Salt

METHOD

- *Blend all the ingredients with a little water into a smooth paste.*
- *Serve mango chutney with poha cutlets and spiced cabbage.*

Coriander Leaf Soup[*]
(Serves Two)

Coriander leaf soup is a good digestive appetizer, which has a cooling effect on the body. It is an anti-inflammatory and antiseptic, and as it strengthens the nervous system, it is very good for balancing the vata dosha.

INGREDIENTS
½ cup of coriander leaf (cilantro/leaves or dhania), chopped
1 big onion
1 tablespoonful of butter
8 corns pepper, powdered
1-inch piece of ginger
8 cloves of garlic
Salt to taste
Lemon to taste

METHOD
- Cut the onions and coriander leaves.
- Make the ginger-garlic paste.
- Powder the pepper corns.
- Add butter to the sauce pan, add ginger-garlic paste, onion and sauté until onion turns golden-brown, then add chopped coriander and sauté for three to four minutes and allow to cool.
- Blend the above and filter.
- Add pepper, salt to the filtered soup and boil.
- Add lemon, garnish with finely chopped coriander leaves and serve hot.

Tweak for Your Dosha:
Pitta – reduce or avoid garlic
In summer – reduce quantity of ginger, garlic and pepper to half

---

[*] Contributed by Indus Valley Ayurveda

9

Grishma Ritu

MEALS TO PACIFY HEAT AND MILD DRYNESS IN THE ENVIRONMENT

Grishma Ritu is the summer season lasting from approximately the middle of May to July. During this season, the days are longer and the sun's energy becomes increasingly powerful. Kapha decreases in the environment and vata begins to gradually increase day by day.

During this season, it's a good idea to shower with cool water and wear lighter, cotton clothing. In terms of food and eating habits, breakfast should be light consisting of fruit, fruit juices and cooling drinks like sherbet and lassis. All of these can also serve as mid-morning or mid-afternoon snacks. Dinner should be light, and although lunch is considered the main meal of the day, it should not be overly heavy either.

Avoid wine, alcohol and heating foods. Instead, this is the time to drink cold water, sugarcane juice and other fresh fruit juices. Add cardamom powder for flavour and additional cooling.

Eat foods that are sweet, light, oily and make sure you drink plenty of cooling liquids.

Suggested meal combinations for Grishma Ritu:

- Almond soup infused with olive oil, fig chutney, kokum cooler
- Peanut and sesame/coconut stuffed okra with rice or barley, kesar-pista lassi
- Plantain slices topped with a spicy dressing, puris
- Pumpkin and dal soup with dashmool dressing, amla sherbet
- Buttermilk curry with bulgur wheat, spiced eggplant
- Vata snack time: fig and oatmeal cookies, cold vata/pitta tea

RECIPES

Buttermilk Curry
(Serves Two to Three)

This is one of my favourite buttermilk curries. In Punjabi households, dairy products have always been at the forefront and at the centre of the dining table.

INGREDIENTS
1 tablespoonful of ghee
1½ teaspoonsful of black mustard seeds
½ teaspoonful of cumin seeds
½ teaspoonful of turmeric
2 medium green onions, trimmed, sliced lengthwise in half and then crosswise into 1-inch lengths
1 green cayenne chilli, minced
¼ water, if using yoghurt
1 cup of plain yoghurt

Salt
1 tablespoonful of coriander leaves, chopped

METHOD
- *In a wok (or karhai) heat ghee over medium-high flame.*
- *Toss in the mustard seeds. When most of them have popped, add the cumin and turmeric and stir.*
- *Lower the heat to medium, add the green onions and chillies, and stir-fry for about three minutes, until softened.*
- *Stir in the water. Reduce the heat to low, pour in the yogurt and stir until warmed, but do not bring to boil. Add salt.*
- *Transfer to a serving bowl and top with the coriander. Serve hot.*

Kesar-Pista Lassi

(Serves Four)

This cool and soothing lassi combines the goodness of dry fruit and yoghurt.

INGREDIENTS
A few strands of saffron (kesar)
2 tablespoonsful of pistachios, chopped
3 cups of fresh yoghurt
4 teaspoonsful of jaggery

METHOD
- *Dry roast the saffron strands for about ten seconds.*
- *Add two tablespoonsful of milk, mix gently and then set aside for about fifteen minutes.*
- *Combine all the ingredients and blend in a mixer for three to four minutes.*
- *Pour into four individual glasses and serve immediately.*

Almond Soup

(Serves Four)

This is my take on a traditional cold soup from Andalusia, Spain. Perfect for balancing vata energies, this is a great soup for the season. If you can have it cool or heated gently, that's fine too.

Ingredients
6 cloves of garlic, peeled
Pepper
Salt
1 cup of almonds, peeled
1 cup of brown bread crumbs
1 cup of extra virgin olive oil
4¼ cup of water or weak dosha tea
3 tablespoonsful of lemon juice
¼ cup of white grapes

Method
- *Crush garlic cloves with the pepper and salt, preferably with a mortar and pestle.*
- *Soak the breadcrumbs in water, then drain and add with the almonds to the garlic mixture. Continue crushing in mortar and pestle.*
- *Gradually pour in the olive oil while crushing and continue until the mixture is fluid and smooth.*
- *Slowly add the water until the desired density.*
- *Add lemon and extra salt if necessary.*
- *Garnish with a swirl of olive oil and a few grapes*

Tweak for Your Dosha:
Instead of a water base, use a weak dosha tea based on the dosha you are trying to balance

Fig Chutney
(Serves Four)

Although dried figs are available all year round, the sweet, fleshy earthiness of fresh figs is an ideal vata-balancer. You can find figs in the market twice a year – usually from May–June and then again in December through January.

INGREDIENTS

1 cup of lemon juice

¼ pound of jaggery*

1 small onion, chopped

1-inch piece of fresh ginger, chopped

1½ teaspoonsful of yellow mustard seeds

¼ lemon, zested

½-inch piece of cinnamon stick

1¾ teaspoonsful of salt

¼ teaspoonful of ground pippali

⅛ teaspoonful of ground cloves

2 cups of firm, slightly under-ripe fresh figs, rinsed, stems removed and halved

METHOD

- In a large saucepan, combine the lemon juice, jaggery, onion, ginger, mustard seeds, lemon zest, cinnamon stick, salt, pippali and cloves and bring to a boil.
- Reduce the heat to a simmer and cook until the mixture is thickened and reduced by ²/₃, forming a thick syrup.
- Add the figs and cook gently until they are very soft, nearly falling apart and most of the liquid they've given off has evaporated, for about thirty minutes.
- Transfer the chutney to another container and allow to cool before serving.

Tweak for Your Dosha

Add dosha churna as required

Peanut and Sesame/Coconut-stuffed Okra

(Serves Four)

This is my take on bharwan bhindi, stuffed a little differently to balance the vata dosha.

---

* If the figs are quite sweet, you do not need to add jaggery. I generally just omit.

INGREDIENTS

3 cups of okra (bhindi)
1 onion, sliced
1½ cups of coarsely ground peanuts
¼ cup of sesame seeds (til)
1½ teaspoonsful of red chilli powder
6 teaspoonsful of ghee
1 teaspoonful of garlic, chopped
5 to 6 curry leaves
1 teaspoonful of amchur powder
1 teaspoonful of vata churna
1½ teaspoonsful of coriander powder
Salt to taste
¼ cup of water

METHOD

- Wash bhindi in cold water and pat dry using a paper towel.
- Remove top part of bhindi and slit lengthwise.
- Mix peanuts, sesame seeds, vata churna, red chilli powder, coriander powder, salt, and amchur in a bowl, mix well.
- Add ¼ cup of water and mix well to make a thick paste.
- Stuff this mixture through the slits into the bhindi.
- Coat pan with ghee and shallow fry bhindi on all sides until it is evenly cooked.
- Heat ghee in a pan, add mustard seeds, cumin seeds, curry leaves, chopped garlic and sauté until garlic turns a nice golden colour.
- Add sliced onion and fry until it changes colour.
- Add remaining stuffing and roast for three to four minutes.
- Add cooked bhindi, mix and cook for five minutes.
- Garnish with coriander leaves.

Tweak for Your Dosha:

Pitta – replace vata churna with pitta churna. replace peanuts with coconut
Kapha – replace vata churna with kapha churna

Plantain with Spicy Dressing
(Serves Two to Three)

INGREDIENTS
1 large plantain, almost ripe
Ghee
Salt

DIP
¼ cup of yoghurt
¼ to ½ teaspoonful of red chilli powder
½ teaspoonful of honey
½ teaspoonful of lemon zest
1 pinch of vata churna
Salt to taste

MAKE THE PLANTAINS
- ♪ *Using a sharp knife, chop off the top and bottom of the plantains.*
- ♪ *Cut two or three vertical slits in the skin of the plantain. Peel the plantain, being careful not to gouge out any of the flesh.*
- ♪ *Cut the plantain into ½-inch thick slices.*
- ♪ *Heat a heavy-bottomed cast iron pan or skillet over medium-high heat.*
- ♪ *Pour in about ½ teaspoonful of ghee and heat until you can feel heat coming off the pan.*
- ♪ *Add the plantains to the oil and cook for four to five minutes on each side, or until golden-brown and darker on the edges.*
- ♪ *Place on top of a few paper towels to drain and crisp up. Sprinkle with salt.*

DIP
- ♪ *Mix all of the ingredients together and add salt to taste. Serve with the fried plantains.*

Tweak for Your Dosha:
Replace churna with pitta or kapha churna

Red Pumpkin and Dal Soup with Dashmool Dressing*
(Serves Four)

The ingredients make this ideal for the season, especially when served with something starchy like plantain fritters.

INGREDIENTS

1 small onion, peeled and chopped
2 cloves of garlic, peeled and crushed
1-inch piece of ginger, peeled and shredded
1 cup plus 2 tablespoonsful of split red lentils (lal masoor vibhajit)
3 teaspoonsful of fresh turmeric, chopped
1¼ teaspoonsful of chilli powder
1 small red pumpkin (lal bhopla)
¼ cup of cilantro, chopped
Salt and freshly ground black pepper

ONION-DASHMOOL TOPPING

2 medium onions, peeled and cut into rings
3 tablespoonsful of peanut oil
2 small, hot chilli peppers
2 cloves of garlic
1 teaspoonful of dried dashmool

METHOD

- In a medium-sized, heavy-based saucepan, combine the onions, garlic and ginger.
- Add lentils with six cups of water. Bring to a boil, then turn down the heat to an enthusiastic simmer.
- Stir in the turmeric and chilli powder, season and leave to simmer, covered, for about twenty minutes.
- While the soup is cooking, bring a medium-sized pan of water to a boil. Peel the pumpkin and scoop out the seeds and pulp, then cut the flesh into fat chunks.
- Boil the pumpkin pieces for ten minutes until they are tender enough to pierce with a skewer without much pressure. Drain and set aside.

---

* Soup can be served warm or cool (at room temperature)

- *Cook onion rings in the peanut oil in a shallow pan until they start to turn brown.*
- *Cut the chilli peppers in half, scrape out the seeds and finely slice the flesh.*
- *Peel and finely slice the garlic and add it with the peppers to the onions.*
- *Add dashmool.*
- *Continue cooking until the onions are a deep golden-brown. Set aside*
- *Remove the lid from the lentils and turn up the heat, boiling hard for five minutes.*
- *Remove the pan from the heat, then add the drained pumpkin.*
- *Purée the soup a little at a time in a food processor until smooth, then pour it into a bowl.*
- *Stir in the roughly chopped cilantro and check the seasoning. Add more salt if necessary.*
- *Spoon the onion-dashmool mix on top.*

Date and Tamarind Crêpes

(Serves Eight)

This is my Ayurvedic take on savoury crêpes with Nutella that is a popular dish in France.

INGREDIENTS

1 cup of whole mung
1 cup of long grain rice
½-inch piece of ginger
2 to 3 green chillies
1 teaspoonful of cumin seeds
Ghee
Salt to taste
¼ cup of tamarind, soaked
¼ cup of fresh dates
1 teaspoonful of manjishta powder
½ cup of fresh coconut, ground
½ cup of spring onions, chopped

METHOD

- Rinse and soak the mung beans and rice overnight.
- Grind together ginger, green chillies and cumin seeds.
- Add drained mung beans and rice, salt, water and grind until it forms a smooth batter.
- Heat a flat pan, a griddle or a dosa pan.
- Pour a small amount of batter into the centre of the pan/griddle, then using the bottom of the ladle spread the batter into a large oval shape not more than $1/8$-inch thick.
- Reduce the flame to low as soon as tiny bubbles form across the surface of the dough.
- When the bottom turns crisp and golden brown and the edges loosen, drizzle a little oil along the edges.
- Use a spatula to remove the crêpe from the griddle.
- Repeat with the remaining batter.

SAUCE

- Grind the tamarind water, manjishta powder and dates together into a thick sauce.
- If you prefer a thinner consistency, add some water.
- Spread onto the crêpe and top with grated coconut and spring onions.

Kokum Cooler

(Serves Two Cups)

A perfect antidote to the warm summer days.

INGREDIENTS

2 whole fresh kokum or 4 to 5 dry kokum peels
2 cups of water
3 fresh green chillies
1 fresh red chilli
1 teaspoonful of jaggery (or you can substitute with stevia or molasses, but not honey)
A pinch of asafoetida
Natural rock salt

SEASONING
I tablespoonful of ghee
I teaspoonful of whole mustard seeds
I to 2 of fresh (or dried) red chillies, chopped
I teaspoonful of fresh (or dried) kokum, chopped

METHOD
- *If you are using fresh kokum, squeeze it with your hands in water until it colours the water.*
- *If fresh kokum is not available then you can soak the dry peels in water for about thirty minutes.*
- *Mix the kokum water with salt, jaggery and green chillies.*
- *Dilute the asafoetida in water and add to the mixture.*
- *Then prepare the seasoning: heat the oil and add the mustard seeds.*
- *When the mustard seeds start popping, add the chopped red chilli and dried/fresh kokum pieces.*

SMOOTHIES

Generally I am not in favour of 'sweetening' juices, but if you must, then feel free to add an apple to any of the following green juice recipes. Use a good quality cold-pressed juicer. If, however, you cannot find one then you can use a blender to mix the ingredients and a cheesecloth to separate any pulp from the juice after blending. The trick though is to drink the juice immediately – despite what ready-made juice companies profess about cold-pressed juices keeping fresh in the refrigerator for up to three days, it is key to remember that veggies begin to lose vitality as soon as they are juiced. So drink up quickly.

Coconut Smoothie
(Serves Four)

INGREDIENTS
1 cup of purified water
2 cups of coconut water
1 grapefruit
1 cup grapes
2 tablespoons of coconut meat
2 large handfuls of any leafy green (mustard, amaranth, methi, etc.)
2 large handfuls of lettuce
½ handful of arugula

METHOD
- *Start by blending the water, coconut water, fruit and coconut.*
- *Then add the leafy greens and blend again until smooth.*
- *Mix all the ingredients in the blender until smooth.*
- *Pour the green smoothie into the nut milk bag or cheesecloth. Gently squeeze it in order to separate the juice from the pulp.*

Amla Sherbet
(Serves Three to Four)

INGREDIENTS
1 cup of Indian gooseberry (amla)
½-inch piece ginger
7 to 8 mint leaves
3 cups of water
1 tablespoonful of honey
1½ tablespoonsful of roasted cumin seed powder
1½ tablespoonsful of fennel seed powder
1½ tablespoonsful of chaat masala (optional)
Black salt to taste

METHOD
- *Wash and de-seed the amlas, chop finely.*
- *Wash mint leaves and ginger. Chop them too.*

- *Combine chopped amla, spinach, mint and ginger into a processor. Add a cup of water. Grind until a smooth purée is formed.*
- *Pour the mixture over a strainer or cheesecloth. Squeeze the pulp over the strainer to extract more juice. Discard the pulp.*
- *Add two cups of water to the collected juice. Stir in honey, spices and black salt to taste.*
- *Refrigerated, this one can last a few days.*

Spiced Eggplant

(Serves Four)

INGREDIENTS

¾ cup of olive oil

2 tablespoonsful of lemon peel, chopped

2 cloves of garlic, smashed

2 teaspoonsful, cumin powder

1 teaspoonful of coriander powder

1 teaspoonful of red chilli

¾ teaspoonful of cinnamon powder

½ teaspoonful of red pepper flakes

½ teaspoonful of salt

2 medium eggplants, halved lengthwise

METHOD

- *Preheat oven to 350°F.*
- *Stir in the oil and the next eight ingredients in a small bowl for the spice mix.*
- *With a knife, score each eggplant with half-inch deep diagonal lines criss-crossing each other. Do not cut through the flesh.*
- *Drizzle one tablespoonful of oil over the cut side of each half, allowing it to soak in.*
- *Season lightly with salt.*
- *Spoon spice mix over the eggplant, dividing evenly.*
- *Place eggplants, cut side up, on a rimmed baking sheet.*
- *Roast until soft and very tender in the middle, for about fifty to sixty minutes.*

Fig and Oatmeal Cookies
(Makes Twelve Cookies)

The combination of figs and oats are perfect for balancing vata and pitta alike. You can also substitute the figs for prunes if you like.

INGREDIENTS
1½ cups of oats
1½ cups of almond meal
½ cup of date paste
1 cup dried figs, chopped
3 tablespoonful of coconut oil
½ teaspoonful of vanilla extract
¼ teaspoonful of salt
3 tablespoonful of goji berries
Extra goji berries and oatmeal to garnish

METHOD
- *Combine oats, almond meal, date paste, figs, coconut oil, vanilla extract, salt and goji berries in a food processor.*
- *Shape the dough into cookie-shapes of your choice. The dough will be quite sticky, so round cookies will be the easiest. To prevent the mixture from sticking to your hands, fill a little bowl with some water to wet your fingers.*
- *Place the cookies onto a tray and place in the fridge to 'dry'.*
- *When the outside of the cookies is dry enough, flip the cookies and continue drying in the fridge until the cookies are crusty on the outside and still slightly soft on the inside.*

10

Varsha Ritu

EATING TO PACIFY VATA ELEMENTS IN THE ENVIRONMENT

Varsha Ritu is the monsoon season which starts from approximately the middle of July and goes on till September. During this season, the vata dosha elements are naturally aggravated, and vata being the most volatile of the three doshas, it attempts to push the other doshas off-kilter too and weakens the agni. This implies:

○ You are more prone to illness during this season, so it is best to keep your diet light with easily digestible foods

○ Add honey to juices and foods that are not warm

○ Avoid dairy products in this season

During this season, it's a good idea to avoid long exposure to sunlight and try not to nap during the day. Temper your foods with sweet, sour and salty spices to help pacify the excess vata dosha in the environment. Of course, each meal can be further tweaked to meet your individual dosha type.

Breakfast during the monsoon season should be light, as should dinners. Eat smaller portions and lighter meals through the day rather than overeating at any one meal. Mid-morning and afternoon snacks can count as meals. If you do not want to experiment with too much cooking, then fruits or nuts with honey also make ideal snacks for this season.

Suggested meal combinations for Varsha Ritu:

- ○ Vata snack time: raspberry refresher smoothie and chyawanprash (nutritious herbal jam) cookies
- ○ Vata snack time: seasonal tea and orange cake
- ○ Dal kebabs, sautéed bean sprouts
- ○ Tulsi sweet potatoes, ragi rotis
- ○ Oat soup, banana-cucumber salad
- ○ Cocoa smoothie, date and tamarind crêpes
- ○ Dosa, sesame chutney, haldi and ginger swaras with honey

RECIPES

Dosa

(Serves Two to Three)

While traditionally made with rice, this recipe uses millet.

INGREDIENTS
1 cup of whole green mung, preferably sprouted
½ cup of spinach, washed and chopped
½ cup of millet
2 cups of water
½ teaspoonful of cumin seeds (jeera)
¼ teaspoonful of black pepper, crushed
½ teaspoonful of freshly grated ginger

FILLING
2 carrots, grated (optional)*

---

* Feel free to replace carrots with zucchini or broccoli.

I bunch of coriander, washed and chopped
¼ cup of coconut (fresh or dry), chopped
½ cup of fresh haldi, chopped
½ teaspoonful of salt

METHOD

- *Wash and soak the mung beans and millet together for five to six hours or overnight.*
- *Drain the grains and grind in the blender along with spinach.*
- *Add water little by little in between grinding to achieve a fine consistency and make a semi-liquid batter.*
- *Leave the batter to ferment for two to three hours.*
- *Add cumin, pepper, ginger and salt and mix thoroughly.*
- *Heat the skillet on medium flame.*
- *Apply ½ teaspoonful of ghee to grease the skillet.*
- *Take two to three tablespoonful of batter and spread it evenly on the skillet like pancake.*
- *Cook for one to two minutes and when it gets crisp and brown underneath, carefully flip it over and cook the other side.*
- *Sprinkle with a little grated carrots, coconut, fresh haldi and cilantro.*
- *Eat warm and serve with a chutney of your choice.*

Tweak for Your Dosha:

Vata – add nuts while grinding
Pitta – serve with salad or green juice and have with amla jam or coconut chutney
Kapha – serve with kokum cooler

Raspberry Refresher Smoothie
(Serves Two)

INGREDIENTS

I cup of raspberries
I banana
I tablespoonful of fresh mint
I tablespoonful of coconut oil
1¼ cup of coconut water
I teaspoonful of vidari kanda powder

3 fresh brahmi leaves,
I teaspoonful of honey – optional*

METHOD
☞ *In a blender, combine all the ingredients until smooth.*

Tweak for Your Dosha:
Pitta – replace vidari kanda with manjishta
Kapha – replace vidari kanda with chitrak root powder

Banana Cucumber Salad

(Serves Two to Three)

This is another great summer-time salad made of raw foods.
You can grate or finely chop the coconut and cucumber or
you can leave the pieces large and chunky. Personally, I prefer
the latter. Make sure you use lime rather than lemon juice.

INGREDIENTS
2 bananas
Lime juice
2 tablespoonsful of sunflower seeds
15 grams of coconut, grated or chopped
2 cucumbers, medium size
Salt and chillies to taste
I tablespoonful of honey – optional*
Mint for garnish

METHOD
☞ *Slice the bananas.*
☞ *Grate or chop the cucumber.*
☞ *In a bowl, add the bananas, cucumber, coconut and peanuts. Add the lime juice, chillies (and optional honey) and toss well.*
☞ *Adjust seasoning and garnish with mint.*

Tweak for Your Dosha:
Vata and kapha – replace the sunflowers seeds with two
tablespoonsful of roasted and crushed peanuts

Orange Cake
(Serves Six)

An intense, flavourful cake. Perfect for the season.

INGREDIENTS
1 cup of whole wheat flour
½ of ragi flour
¾ cup of jaggery
1 teaspoonful of baking soda
½ teaspoonful of baking powder
1 cup of fresh squeezed orange juice with pulp
⅓ cup of ghee
2 tablespoonsful of orange peel/zest, grated

METHOD
- *Grease a cake pan. Heat oven to 180°F. Mix the dry ingredients together – wheat, ragi, jaggery, baking soda and baking powder.*
- *Add the ghee and orange zest. Add orange juice. Stir just enough to combine the ingredients without beating – do not over-mix. Pour into the prepared baking pan. Bake for forty to forty-five minutes or until the cake tests are done.*

Tweak for Your Dosha
Pitta and kapha – experiment using jowar and bajra flour instead

Dal Kebabs
(Serves Four)

INGREDIENTS
2 cups of split bengal gram (chana dal), soaked
Ghee
Salt to taste
¼ of caraway seed powder (shahi jeera)
½-inch piece of ginger, chopped
2 green chillies, chopped
1 onion, chopped
½ teaspoonful of red chillies, crushed

2 tablespoonsful of fresh coriander leaves, chopped
2 teaspoonsful of gram flour (besan)

METHOD

- *Drain dal and grind half of it coarsely in a mixer. Set aside.*
- *Grind the remaining dal finely and add to the coarsely ground dal.*
- *In a kadai, heat ghee. Add salt, caraway seeds, ginger, green chillies, onion, crushed red chillies and coriander leaves, and mix well.*
- *Add gram flour and continue mixing.*
- *Dampen your fingers and take small portions of the mixture, flatten slightly and then gently drop into hot oil.*
- *Deep fry on medium heat until half-done. Drain on absorbent paper.*
- *Serve immediately with garlic and chives chutney.*

Tulsi Sweet Potatoes

(Serves Four)

INGREDIENTS

4 medium sweet potatoes, peeled and cut into 1½-inch rounds
3 tablespoonsful of olive oil
1 tablespoonful of fresh oregano leaves, plus a few sprigs for garnish
3 tablespoonsful of fresh tulsi leaves, chopped, plus a few sprigs for garnish
2 small cloves of garlic, minced
¼ teaspoonful of crushed red chilli flakes
1 teaspoonful of coarse salt

METHOD

- *Preheat oven to 400°F.*
- *In a medium bowl, toss the sweet-potato rounds with olive oil, oregano, tulsi, garlic, red chilli flakes and salt.*
- *Transfer to a baking sheet, garnish with oregano sprigs and tulsi florets and place in oven.*
- *Roast until tender and starting to brown, for forty to forty-five minutes.*
- *Transfer to a platter and serve.*

Tweak for Your Dosha:
Feel free to add pitta or kapha churna as required

Chyawanprash Thumbprint Cookies
(Serves Six to Eight pieces)

INGREDIENTS

BASE
¼ cup of barley
¼ cup of millet
½ teaspoonful of salt
Xanthan gum for binding (if you cannot find this, you can
substitute it with egg)
½ teaspoonful of jaggery
A pinch of cinnamon

METHOD
- *Mix together and divide into cookies on a grease plate; cook for ten to fifteen minutes only until warm and solid. Thumbprint each cookie when still warm.*
- *Spoon chyawanprash into the thumb print.*
- *Sprinkle white sesame seeds on top.*

Garlic and Chives Chutney
(Serves Four)

INGREDIENTS
1 cup of chives with the garlic buds, chopped
½ cup of coriander leaves, chopped
1 or 2 green chilies, chopped
1 teaspoonful of lemon juice
1 teaspoonful of chaat masala powder
½ teaspoonful of roasted cumin powder
Kala namak

METHOD
- *In a blender/grinder, blend all the ingredients until smooth.*

- *Add very little water while blending.*
- *Serve the garlic chives chutney with any main staple food.*

Tweak for Your Dosha:
Pitta – reduce garlic chives to ½ cup of garlic and increase coriander to 1 cup worth

Bael Jam
(Serves One Jar)

INGREDIENTS
1 kg of ripe bael (bilwa)
3 cups of jaggery
Lemon juice to taste
2 teaspoonsful of cardamom powder
1 teaspoon of salt

METHOD
- *Seed and shell the bael and remove the stringy parts.*
- *Cut the fruit into small pieces.*
- *Make a sugar syrup of one-thread consistency.*
- *Add lemon juice, salt and the bael pieces.*
- *Continue cooking until the syrup thickens.*
- *Add cardamom powder and mix.*
- *Cool and store the jam in an airtight jar.*

Brahmi Tambuli*
(Serves Two to Three)

Brahmi tambuli is an ideal dish for the summer. Avoid at night though or on cloudy days when there is a tendency to have nasal, chest congestion, or flu. Acceptable for all constitutions.

---

* Contributed by Indus Valley Ayurveda.

INGREDIENTS
½ cup of brahmi leaves
¼ cup of coconut, grated
2 cups of buttermilk
¼ teaspoonful of cumin seeds (jeera)
1 green chilli
Salt to taste

SEASONING
1 teaspoonful of oil/ghee
¼ teaspoonful of mustard seeds
A pinch of asafoetida (hing)
4 curry leaves

METHOD
- *Grind together the brahmi leaves, grated coconut, cumin seeds, green chilli with a little buttermilk. Prepare a very smooth paste with this.*
- *Mix the remaining buttermilk with the above ground mixture, add salt and mix well.*
- *Prepare the seasoning by heating oil, adding the mustard seeds, curry leaves, broken red chilli and finally, hing.*
- *Pour this seasoning over the tambuli prepared.*
- *Serve it at room temperature.*

Broken Wheat Upma*

(Serves Four)

An ideal breakfast recipe for all seasons, broken wheat upma is rich in dietary fibre and energy. Wheat is considered a nourishing and strengthening food. It's properties are heavy, oily, sweet and cooling in nature and helps in balancing vata – pitta. As it is fairly heavy to digest, it is best not to over consume.

---

* Contributed by Indus Valley Ayurveda.

INGREDIENTS

½ cup of broken wheat
1 tablespoonful of cooking oil
¼ teaspoonful of mustard seeds
2 green chillies, chopped
2 strands of curry leaves
½ cup of onions, chopped
½-inch piece of ginger
¼ cup of carrots, chopped
Salt to taste
2 tablespoons of coriander leaves, finely chopped

METHOD

- *Clean and wash the broken wheat thoroughly, cook the broken wheat in two cups of water for five minutes.*
- *Drain the excess water and keep aside.*
- *Heat the oil in a pressure cooker and add the mustard seeds.*
- *When the mustard seeds splutter, add the chopped onions, ginger, curry leaves and sauté for three minutes, then add carrot and green chillies and sauté on a medium flame for five minutes.*
- *Add the broken wheat, salt and 1¼ cups of water, mix well and pressure cook for two whistles.*
- *Once the pressure settles, open the lid and garnish with coriander leaves and keep aside to cool slightly.*

Tweak for Your Dosha:
Vata and pitta – as is
Kapha – add garlic and ginger

Kokum Rasam*

(Serves Two)

Kokum rasam is a good digestive/appetizer in addition to being an excellent source of antioxidants and has an anti-inflammatory effect. It is highly beneficial for piles, pain,

---

* Contributed by Indus Valley Ayurveda.

flatulence, constipation, heatstroke, nausea and fever. It is known as the 'cool king' of Indian fruits. Furthermore, it helps in weight loss, stimulates the liver and is cardioprotective. It makes the dhaatu *agni* functioning *(the digestion in the dhaatus)* strong. Ideal for all constitutions and seasons. It can be had as a soup or with rice. Avoid milk or any milk-based dessert during that particular meal.

INGREDIENTS
7 to 8 kokum fruits (garcinia)
1 teaspoonful of jaggery powder
¼ teaspoonful of mustard seeds
½ teaspoonful of cumin (jeera)
5 pepper corns, ground
1 dry red chilli
4 to 5 curry leaves
4 cloves of garlic, crushed
1 teaspoonful of ghee
¼ teaspoonful of asafoetida (hing)
Salt to taste

METHOD
- *Add two cups water to the kokum and boil for ten minutes on medium flame.*
- *Add salt and jaggery and boil for two to three minutes and keep aside.*
- *Seasoning: heat ghee in a pan and add mustard seeds, allow to splutter, then add jeera, curry leaves, garlic, asafoetida, pepper and red chilli.*
- *Mix the seasoning to the kokum rasam.*
- *Serve hot.*

Tweak for Your Dosha:
Pitta – reduce garlic and pepper to half the quantity

PART III

Resources

Appendix – I

Here is a list of common herbs and spices used in Ayurveda:

AMALAKI

Also known as amla or the Indian gooseberry, amalaki is a small fruit, pale green or yellowish-green in colour. Sour in taste, sour in post-digestive effect and hot in potency (virya). It has antioxidant, diuretic, antiviral, antimicrobial, antipyretic, anti-inflammatory and antianaemia properties. It balances all doshas, especially pitta.

ASHWAGANDHA

Also known as *withania somnifera*, this plant root is known for its tonic, rejuvenating, aphrodisiac properties and has a positive effect on the nervous system. Sharp and pungent in taste, it balances vata and kapha.

BHUMYAMALAKI

Bhumyamalaki as known as *phyllantus amarus*, is the classic Ayurvedic herb for the liver. It is very bitter, astringent and sweet in taste. It has a sweet post-digestive effect and cooling potency. It is soothing, cleansing and balances pitta and kapha.

BRAHMI

Also known by the name of bacopa or Indian gotu kola, brahmi is a small, creeping herb with numerous branches. Bitter in taste, sweet in post-digestive effect and with a cold potency, brahmi has antioxidant and anticancer properties. It helps restore memory, higher cognitive and neurological functions. It balances all three doshas, especially vata and pitta.

DASHMOOL

Dashmool, or ten different roots, is a nourishing muscle tonic that strengthens the body and calms the nerves. Dashmool promotes healthy expectoration and respiration while supporting the proper function of the lungs and nervous system. Astringent and sweet in taste, it is pungent in post-digestive effect and warming in potency. It balances vata and kapha.

DHANYAKA

Also known as coriander or *coriandrum sativum*, dhaniya has been used as a flavouring agent and a medicinal plant since ancient times. In Ayurveda, both the seeds and the leaves of this plant are used for treating a number of health problems. Sweet in post-digestive effect with a hot potency, it is known for its tonics and digestive properties. It alleviates all three doshas.

GUDUCHI

Guduchi, also known as *tinospora cordifolia*, is considered a prime rejuvenating and healing herb in Ayurvedic medicine. It has divine origins in ancient Hindu texts. Its other name, Amrita, is known as the nectar of the gods. It is excellent for getting rid of deep-rooted imbalances in the body. With a bitter, pungent and astringent taste, it balances the pitta dosha and combines well with shatavari and ashwagandha as a general wellness tonic.

HARIDRA

Commonly known as turmeric or as *curcuma longa* in Latin, haridra has a bright yellow colour and is hot, bitter and astringent in taste. It has anti-inflammatory, antiseptic, antibacterial, antioxidant, antiviral and antifungal properties. It balances all three doshas.

KUMARI

Also known as aloe vera, this is a succulent and mucilaginous plant that can grow upto forty inches in height. The thick and heavy green leaves contain a precious healing gel that provides many health benefits. Bitter and sweet in taste, sweet in post-digestive effect and cold in potency, aloe vera gel has disinfectant, antibiotic, antimicrobial, germicidal, antibacterial, antiseptic, antifungal and antiviral properties. It alleviates all three doshas.

MANJISTHA

Popularly known as red madder root, manjistha is a climber, usually growing over other bushes or trees. The roots as well as the stems are used for medicinal purposes. It has antibacterial and diuretic properties. One of the most powerful blood purifiers for skin diseases and for improving the complexion, it is bitter, astringent and sweet in taste, pungent in post-digestive effect with a hot potency. It pacifies all three doshas, especially pitta.

NIMBA

Also known as azadirachta indica, Indian lilac or margosa, neem has been used for centuries because of its medicinal properties. It has antibacterial, antifungal, antiulcer, blood purifying and antipyretic, antiparasitic, antiseptic and antiemetic properties. Various parts of the tree are used in Ayurveda for treating a plethora of health problems. Bitter and astringent in taste, it is pungent in post-digestive effect and cold in potency. It balances the pitta and kapha doshas.

PIPPALI

Pippali is a powerful rejuvenating herb that strengthens and nourishes the body. It stimulates metabolism, burns natural toxins and helps maintain a healthy digestive environment. It is an excellent tonic for the lungs, supporting clear and comfortable breathing. Pungent in taste, sweet in post-digestive effect and hot in potency, it balances vata and kapha.

TULSI

Also known as holy basil or *ocimum sanctum*, this plant is actually considered sacred in India. It is a small plant with small leaves, hairy stems and a soothing fragrance. It has demulcent, expectorant, anticatarrhal, antispasmodic, diaphoretic, digestive stimulating, antimicrobial, antifungal, antiparasitic and antibacterial properties. Pungent and bitter in taste, pungent in post-digestive effect and heating in potency, it is a stimulant, aromatic herb that effectively reduces fever. It balances vata and kapha.

YASHTI MADHU

Yasthi madhu or liquorice root has been used as a powerful medicine in both Ayurveda and various other forms of modern medicine. Liquorice root works as an expectorant, antispasmodic, anti-inflammatory, laxative, hypertensive, antiulcer, estrogenic, antibacterial, antifungal and immune stimulant. The sweet and cooling taste of the liquorice root balances the pitta dosha.

APPENDIX – 2

List of Resources

AYURVEDIC HERBS AND PRODUCTS

Under the Mango Tree
http://utmt.in/

The Altitude Store
http://www.thealtitudestore.
com/

Organic India
http://organicindiashop.com/
http://organicindia.co.in/

Satvik Shop
http://satvikshop.com/

Always Ayurveda
http://www.alwaysayurveda.
com/

Vedic Gift Shop
http://www.vedicgiftshop.
com/patanjali-divya-products/
patanjali-ayurvedic-chikitsalaya-
center-list/

The Organic Garden
http://www.organicgarden.
co.in/

AYURVEDIC SPAS/PANCHA KARMA CENTRES

Indus Valley Ayurvedic Center
http://www.ayurindus.com/

Vishwanath Panchakarma
Ayurveda Centre
www.panchkarma.org

Kerala Ayurvedic Healthcare
www.keralaayurvedichealthcare.
com/ayurveda/
ayurveda_centers.htm

Arya Vaidya Shala
http://aryavaidyasala.com

VCC Ayurveda
www.vccayurveda.com

Jiva Ayurveda
www.jiva.com

YOGA/AYURVEDA CENTRES

Krishnamacharya Centre
www.kym.org

Sivananda Yoga Vedanta Centre
www.sivananda.org/trivandrum

Satyananda Yoga Mandiram
www.satyanandayogacenter.
com

Parmarth Niketan
www.parmarth.com

AYURVEDA RETREATS

New Ideal Panchakarma Centre
www.panchakarmakerala.com

Kandamkulathy Ayur Soukhyam
Ayurvedic Resort
www.ayursoukhyam.com

Soukya
www.soukya.com

Kalarikovilakom
www.cghearth.com